'CRELLIN SCHOOL'

WILLIAM K. DURR • JEAN M. LE PERE • BESS NIEHAUS

CONSULTANT • **PAUL McKEE**

LINGUISTIC ADVISOR • **JACK E. KITTELL**

REWARDS

HOUGHTON MIFFLIN COMPANY • BOSTON

ATLANTA · DALLAS · GENEVA, ILLINOIS · HOPEWELL, NEW JERSEY · PALO ALTO

Acknowledgments

For each of the selections listed below, grateful acknowledgment is made for permission to adapt and/or reprint copyrighted material, as follows:

"About the Teeth of Sharks" from *You Read to Me, I'll Read to You* by John Ciardi. Copyright © 1962 The Curtis Publishing Company. Published by J. B. Lippincott Company.

"After the Party," from *Jonathon Blake* by William Wise. Copyright © 1956 by William Wise. Reprinted by permission of Brandt & Brandt.

"Anyone Could, But." From *Act It Out* by Bernice Wells Carlson. Copyright 1956 by Pierce and Washabaugh. Used by permission of Abingdon Press.

Bascombe, the Fastest Hound Alive. Copyright © 1958 by George J. W. Goodman. Reprinted by permission of William Morrow and Company, Inc., Publishers.

"Bedtime" from *Poems for Children* by Eleanor Farjeon. Copyright 1933, 1961 by Eleanor Farjeon. Published in the United States by J. B. Lippincott Company. British rights granted by David Higham Associates, Ltd.

"The Boy and the Whistle" by Elizabeth Ireland, published by Humpty-Dumpty's Magazine, Parents' Magazine Enterprises, March, 1954, reprinted by permission of the author.

"Different" by Jo Carr, reprinted with the author's permission.

Down, Down the Mountain by Ellis Credle. © 1934 by Thomas Nelson & Sons. © renewed 1961 by Ellis Credle.

Evan's Corner by Elizabeth Starr Hill. Text copyright © 1967 by Elizabeth Starr Hill. Illustrations copyright © 1967 by Nancy Grossman. Reprinted by permission of Holt, Rinehart and Winston, Inc. and Brandt & Brandt.

"Every Time I Climb a Tree." From *Every Time I Climb a Tree* by David McCord, by permission of Atlantic-Little, Brown and Co. Copyright 1952 by David McCord.

"Ice Cream Trouble" by Jane Lear Talley. From *New Poems for Children*. Reprinted by permission of Hart Publishing Company.

"Jonathan Bing." From *Jonathan Bing* by Beatrice Curtis Brown. Reprinted by permission of Lothrop, Lee & Shepard Co., Inc. Copyright 1936 by Oxford University Press. Copyright © renewed 1964 by Beatrice Curtis Brown.

Just Like Abraham Lincoln, by Bernard Waber. © 1964, by Bernard Waber. Used by permission of Houghton Mifflin Company.

"Maps" by Dorothy Brown Thompson, copyright 1935, used by permission of the author.

"Meet Miki Takino." Adaptation of *Meet Miki Takino* by Helen Copeland. Reprinted by permission of Lothrop, Lee & Shepard Co., Publishers. Copyright © 1963 by Lothrop, Lee & Shepard Co., Inc.

"Mr. Picklepaw's Popcorn." Adaptation of *Mr. Picklepaw's Popcorn* by Ruth Adams. Reprinted by permission of Lothrop, Lee & Shepard Co. Copyright © 1965 by Lothrop, Lee & Shepard Co., Inc.

"Picnic by the Sea." From *Windy Morning*, copyright, 1953, by Harry Behn. Reprinted by permission of Harcourt, Brace & World, Inc.

"Punia and the King of the Sharks." Text reprinted from *Punia and the King of the Sharks*, by Beverly Mohan. Copyright © 1964 by Follett Publishing Co. and used by their permission.

"The Quarrel" from *Poems for Children* by Eleanor Farjeon. Copyright 1933, 1961 by Eleanor Farjeon. Published by J. B. Lippincott Company and David Higham Associates, Ltd.

"Rain Poem" by Elizabeth Coatsworth. Reprinted with permission of the MacMillan Company from *Poems* by Elizabeth Coatsworth. © by The MacMillan Company 1957.

"Saturday Surprise," by Jean Fritz. Copyright © 1966 by Jean Fritz. From *Round About the City*, compiled by the Child Study Association of America. Thomas Y. Crowell Company, New York, publishers.

Spiders Are Spinners by Ellsworth Rosen, excerpt used by permission of Houghton Mifflin Company.

"Sunning" from *A World to Know* by James S. Tippett. Copyright 1933 Harper & Brothers. Used with permission of Harper & Row, Publishers.

"There Isn't Time" from *Poems for Children* by Eleanor Farjeon. Copyright 1933, 1961 by Eleanor Farjeon. Published in the United States by J. B. Lippincott Company. British rights granted by David Higham Associates, Ltd.

"Washing" by John Drinkwater. From the book *More About Me*. Copyright: First Impression, October, 1929; Second Impression, November, 1929. Reprinted by permission of Samuel French, Inc.

Book cover, title page, and magazine covers by Ikki Matsumoto.
Illustrators: Angela Adams (pp. 34–51), Marietta Brockmann (pp. 172–173), Marc Brown (pp. 71–81), Kevin Callahan (pp. 7–31), Tom Cooke (pp. 246–254), Lou Cunette (p. 174), Dan Dickas (p. 167), Lois Elhert (p. 119), Ed Emberley (pp. 52–54, 56–57, 82–84, 144–146, 170–171, 240–243, 255–258), Les Gray (pp. 142–143), Nancy Grossman (pp. 87–118), Suzette Hillery (pp. 32–33), Elaine Livermore (pp. 140–141), David McPhail (pp. 60–70, 244–245), Michael Milan (pp. 209, 216–239), Sara Mintz (p. 139), Alfred Olschewski (pp. 259–288), Laurence Scott (p. 55), Teco Slagboom (pp. 175–186), Kyuzo Tsugami (pp. 189–208), Joe Veno (pp. 120, 168–169), Eric Von Schmidt (pp. 147–166), Bernard Waber (pp. 121–138), Cecile Webster (pp. 58–59).
Photographers: Werner Stoy, Camera Hawaii, Inc. (pp. 210–215).

1973 IMPRESSION

Contents

TREASURES

SMILES

SOUNDS

TREASURES

TREASURES

BASCOMBE

THE FASTEST HOUND ALIVE

by George Goodman

Once there was a farmhouse by a country
road. It had a big back porch. On the lowest
step of this porch lived a basset hound.

He had very long ears, so long they drooped on the ground most of the time. He had short stubby legs. They were bent like horseshoes.

His name was Bascombe. He belonged to Mr. Winston.

At night he slept in the kitchen, and sometimes he ate there. But most of the day he lay on the bottom step and slept.

If anyone called him, he opened one eye just
the tiniest bit. Every once in a while a
caterpillar walked across his nose, and then
he opened both eyes. But he closed them
again, once the caterpillar was safely across.

One day two rabbits named Herbert and
Sam came by. They had just had lunch
in the garden, and now they were taking a walk.

"Hi, Bascombe," said Herbert. "You look
sad. Are you sad about something?"

Bascombe's head dropped even lower, and
one of his ears drooped off the bottom step.

"Yup," he said. "I'm going to be sold."

"Sold!" said Sam. "Why, you're the best dog
around! You're the only dog that doesn't chase
us and lets us have a little lunch."

"Why are you going to be sold?" Herbert asked.

Bascombe opened one eye just the tiniest bit. "Mr. Winston says I'm a hunting dog. He wants to take me on the big hunt tomorrow, but I can't run fast enough." Bascombe closed the one eye he had opened.

"Why, running is the easiest thing in the world," said Herbert. "Show him, Sam."

Sam ran off so fast that only the white of his tail could be seen.

"That Sam," said Herbert, "is the fastest rabbit in this countryside. Don't you wish you could run that fast?"

Bascombe didn't even open his eyes. "Nope," he said.

Sam came back a little out of breath.

"Bascombe," said Herbert. "You don't want to be sold, do you?"

"Nope," said Bascombe.

"Then you'll have to learn to run the way the other dogs do," said Herbert.

Bascombe sighed. He opened his eyes just the tiniest bit, and watched a caterpillar walk across his nose.

"We'll teach you how to run," said Sam. "Of course, you won't be able to run as fast as we can. But you'll be as fast as the other dogs and Mr. Winston will keep you. O.K.?"

Bascombe sighed again. "Yup," he said.

So they all went up the hill and down to the fields.

"Now don't use up your breath sniffing and
yapping, the way the other dogs do," said
Herbert. "The real trick in going fast is
to wrinkle your nose like this."

And he wrinkled his nose.

"Then you spread your ears," said Sam,
"and give a big push with your hind legs."

Sam spread his ears and gave a big push
with his hind legs. And then he was out of sight
without really trying. Sam was the fastest
rabbit in the countryside.

"Now you," said Herbert. Bascombe wrinkled
up his nose and pointed it. He spread his ears
and then he gave a big push with his hind legs.
Herbert winked. All he could see of Bascombe
was a blur in the grass and a tail moving
very fast.

Bascombe was really very good. He caught up
with Sam without much trouble at all.
"Now wasn't that easy?" said Sam.
"Yup," said Bascombe.
"And isn't it more fun than sleeping all day?"

"Nope," said Bascombe.

The Hunt

The next morning Mr. Winston's neighbors came over with their dogs. There were fat dogs and thin dogs, tall dogs and small dogs, brown dogs and black dogs, and dogs that were all kind of mixed. They crowded around Bascombe.

"Are you coming with us? With those short stubby legs?" they asked.

"Yup," said Bascombe.

"Don't your ears get in the way?" they said.

"Nope," said Bascombe.

All the dogs put their noses to the ground
and sniffed for a smell. Then they waved their
tails in the air to show how eager
they were. But Bascombe wasn't eager.

All this excitement seemed sillier and sillier.
The dogs yapped and sniffed, and sniffed and
yapped. Finally they got the smell.

Off they went, up the hill and down
toward the fields, with Mr. Winston and all the
neighbors running behind. First came the tall
dogs, and then came the small dogs, and in
between were the dogs that were all kind
of mixed.

They were all yapping and sniffing and waving
their tails, all but Bascombe. He was way, way
behind the others.

Suddenly he thought of a wonderful idea that
might take care of all his problems. But he
would have to be the fastest hound of all
to make it work.

Bascombe wrinkled up his nose and pointed it.
He spread his ears. Then he gave a big push
with his hind legs, and away he went.

He passed the small dogs and the dogs that
were all kind of mixed. He passed the tall dogs,
too. He went so fast that all they could see was
a blur and the top of a tail moving very fast.
The dogs were so surprised that they stopped
their sniffing and yapping and watched him go.

He went straight to the bushes, and out
of the bushes popped a rabbit.

"Bascombe found him!" cried the tall dogs.

"Follow Bascombe!" cried the small dogs.

"Do you see him, Bascombe?" cried the dogs that were all kind of mixed.

"Yup!" cried Bascombe.

He began to chase the rabbit. The rabbit ran across the field very fast, with Bascombe close behind.

Even the tallest dogs could hardly see
the rabbit. All they could see of Bascombe was
a blur and the top of a tail moving very fast.

Some of the small dogs were already puffing.
One or two of the smallest dogs were still
sniffing at the bushes, for they had been too far
behind to see what had happened.

All across the field the rabbit ran, until he
got to his hole in the tree. He popped in.

Sold?

"Good morning, Sam," said Herbert who
was already there. "What's wrong?"

"A pack of dogs has been chasing me," said
Sam. "I'm the fastest rabbit in this countryside,
but one of them is staying right on my tail."

"I don't believe it," said Herbert.

They both popped their heads out of the tree.

Coming across the field were some tall
dogs, and behind them, some other dogs, and
behind *them,* still sniffing and yapping, some
tired small dogs.

Way ahead of the whole pack, nose wrinkled,
ears spread, was — *"Bascombe!"* cried Herbert
and Sam together.

They both jumped out of the tree and away
they went back across the field, with Bascombe
close behind.

The small dogs stopped to rest.

"Who can keep up with Bascombe?" they said. "He doesn't sniff and yap, and he goes too fast. That Bascombe is the fastest hound alive. Let's go chase something slower somewhere else."

The small dogs turned around and went home. Then the dogs that were all kind of mixed stopped.

"Who can keep up with Bascombe?" they said. "He goes too fast. That Bascombe is the fastest hound alive. Let's go chase something slower somewhere else. Like cats, maybe." The dogs that were all kind of mixed turned around and went home.

When the rabbits got back to the bushes,
they ran right through. Bascombe followed close
behind. Most of the other dogs ran
around the bushes. The tallest dog of all tried
to jump over them, but he landed right
in the middle.

"That Bascombe," said the tallest dog, "is just about the fastest hound alive. Who can keep up with Bascombe?"

"We're tired," said the rest of the tall dogs. "Let's go chase something slower somewhere else." The tall dogs ran away, and even Mr. Winston and the other men went home with them.

Now Bascombe was the only one chasing the rabbits. They came around again and popped back into the hole in the tree.

Bascombe sat down outside. "Now I've got you," he said, and he winked his left eye.

"It was your idea to teach him how to run," said Herbert to Sam. "Now we're trapped!"

"Bascombe, it's us," said Sam. "We showed you how to run, remember?"

"Aw," said Bascombe, "I just ran fast to tire
out Mr. Winston. I didn't want to *catch* you."

All three of them looked across the field.
They could just see the last of the tall dogs
going home. Mr. Winston was going home, too.

"I don't care much for all this running," said
Bascombe. "I'm glad it's over."

After dinner that evening, Bascombe was sleeping on the bottom step when Herbert and Sam came by.

"I heard Mr. Winston say he was so tired he'd never go hunting again," said Herbert.

"My idea," said Sam. "Wasn't it, Bascombe?"

"Nope," said Bascombe. "I thought that part up."

"Now you can sleep all the time," said Herbert.

"Yup," said Bascombe.

SUNNING

Old Dog lay in the summer sun
Much too lazy to rise and run.
He flapped an ear
At a buzzing fly.
He winked a half opened
Sleepy eye.
He scratched himself
On an itching spot,
As he dozed on the porch
Where the sun was hot.
He whimpered a bit
From force of habit
While he lazily dreamed
Of chasing a rabbit.
But Old Dog happily lay in the sun
Much too lazy to rise and run.

James S. Tippett

Saturday Surprise

by Jean Fritz

As soon as Peggy woke up, she smiled. The sun was shining. It was just the day to go around the world.

Every Saturday Uncle Charlie took Peggy on a surprise trip.

Once he took her to a bench in the sky. When she looked down, she looked way, way down. At the bottom there were people playing football.

Another time Uncle Charlie took her to the moon.
The moon was on the ceiling of a big room. And the
stars were there, too. Peggy held her head back so long
her neck hurt.

Today Peggy and Uncle Charlie were going around the world. Peggy jumped out of bed and started to dress.

Just then her mother came in. "Peggy," she said, "I have some bad news."

Peggy had one shoe on and one shoe off.

"Uncle Charlie just called. He can't go with you. He has to go out of town," her mother said.

"Well, he can't!" Peggy stamped her foot. "He has to take me around the world."

Then she thought a minute. "How do you go around
the world?"

"In a boat. Uncle Charlie was going to take you in a
boat all around the city. He'll do it another time,"
her mother said.

Peggy knew, of course, that she couldn't go in a boat
all by herself. She knew her mother couldn't take her
because her mother worked on Saturday. And there
was no one else. Peggy and her mother lived alone.

Peggy stamped her foot again.

"I'm sorry," her mother said. "But, anyway, Uncle Charlie has found someone to take you to the park."

"Who?"

"A lady named Miss Finney," said her mother.

"A stranger!" Peggy cried.

"She's a friend of Uncle Charlie's," her mother said.

"Well, she's not *my* friend. She's a stranger." Peggy threw herself across her bed. She didn't like strangers.

"I'm sure Miss Finney is nice," Peggy's mother said.

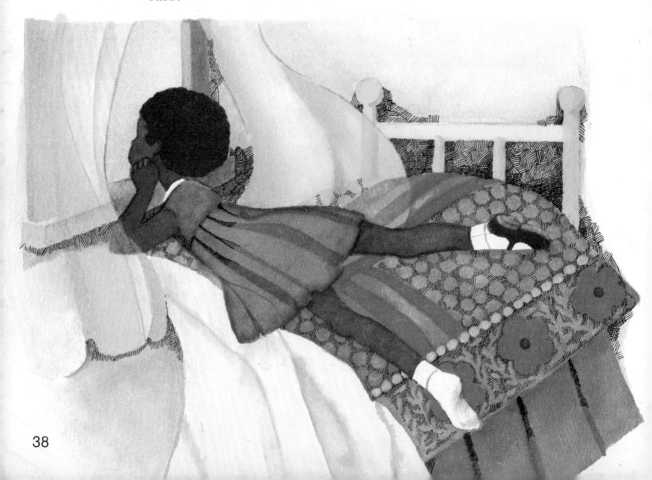

Peggy was sure she wasn't. She knew just what Miss Finney would be like. She would be tall and thin and cross. She would wear black pinchy shoes, and she'd sit on a park bench. She wouldn't go any place. She'd just sit and sit.

When the doorbell rang, Peggy and her mother went to the door. But Peggy wouldn't talk to Miss Finney. She wouldn't look at her.

Of course, she couldn't help seeing the shoes. They were black and pinchy.

Well, she wouldn't even walk with Miss Finney.

When they went out, Peggy walked two steps behind her. Peggy kept her eyes down and followed the black, pinchy shoes.

At the corner they passed a policeman. He was a friend of Peggy's.

"Hi, Peggy," he said. "Where are you going *this* Saturday?"

"No place," Peggy said.

At the next corner they passed the candy-store man.

"Where are you going today, Peggy?" he asked.

"No place," said Peggy.

The black pinchy shoes stopped. They turned. They pointed at the candy-store man.

"We're going visiting," Miss Finney said. "Peggy and I are going to the park and visit some of my friends."

"More strangers!" Peggy thought. "A whole day of strangers!" Well, she wasn't going to look at any of them.

But when they got to the park, Miss Finney didn't speak to any strangers. She didn't stop at any benches. She didn't even stay on the path. She walked right across the grass and under the trees.

It was hard for Peggy to follow the black, pinchy shoes. She could hardly see where she was going. Then suddenly, she found herself at the edge of a pond. The black, pinchy shoes stopped.

Strangers — Friends

"Good morning, Hortense," Miss Finney said. "Peggy and I have brought you some breakfast."

Before she knew what she was doing, Peggy looked up. There was a white swan swimming toward her. And there was Miss Finney. She was tall but she wasn't cross looking.

"Hortense is one of my friends," said Miss Finney. She reached into her handbag and pulled out some bread. "If you'd like, you may feed Hortense," she said. "You can break this up for her."

Peggy threw pieces of bread on the water. She watched as Hortense bent her long, long neck down to eat them.

When the bread was gone, Miss Finney said they were going across the park to visit another friend.

"If he's there," Miss Finney said. "Sometimes he has to go downtown on a job."

This time when Peggy followed Miss Finney, she didn't look at the black, pinchy shoes. She looked up at her. And she wondered who the next friend would be. But she didn't ask.

After a while Miss Finney pointed. "There he is," she said. "Under that tree."

Parked on the side of the road was a shiny black carriage. In front of the carriage, there was a shiny black horse.

"That's Bob," Miss Finney said. She reached into her shopping bag and took out some pieces of sugar. "You may feed him if you like."

Peggy put the sugar on her hand and held her hand way out. When Bob took the sugar, Peggy laughed because it tickled her hand.

When they left Bob, Peggy stepped right up to Miss Finney and walked beside her.

"Now," Miss Finney said. "Here is a dime. I'm looking for a place to spend it. I want to buy a gift for another one of my friends."

Peggy wondered who *this* friend could be. But she didn't ask.

Maybe it was a squirrel, she thought. But Miss Finney walked past four squirrels and didn't speak to any of them.

Maybe it was a dog. But Miss Finney didn't speak to any of the dogs they passed.

Then Miss Finney saw a Balloon Man. "That's what I'm looking for," she said, "a balloon. I think that would make a nice gift."

Peggy wondered what kind of friend would like a balloon, but still she didn't ask.

"I don't know what color to get," said Miss Finney.

Peggy thought red was best, but she didn't say so out loud.

"I think I'd better let my friend pick a balloon for herself," Miss Finney said, and she held out the dime to Peggy. "Go ahead, Peggy," she said. "Pick out the one you like."

"Me?" Peggy said. "Is the balloon for *me*?"

Miss Finney smiled. "Yes, I *said* it was for a friend."

When Peggy and Miss Finney left the Balloon Man, Peggy was carrying a red balloon. She was walking beside Miss Finney, and she was talking to her. Pretty soon they were planning to go to the zoo together.

At the zoo they talked to a goat, and gave peanuts
to a monkey. And all the time Peggy and Miss Finney
talked to each other.

When Peggy got home at the end of the day, she told her mother she hadn't gone *around* the world, but she had gone all *over* it. "And I talked to lots of strangers," she said. "Only guess what?"

"What?" asked her mother.

"The strangers really were friends," Peggy said.

Her mother nodded. "That can happen."

"And guess which one I liked best," asked Peggy.

"Which one?"

Peggy laughed because it was such a surprise.

"Miss Finney," she said.

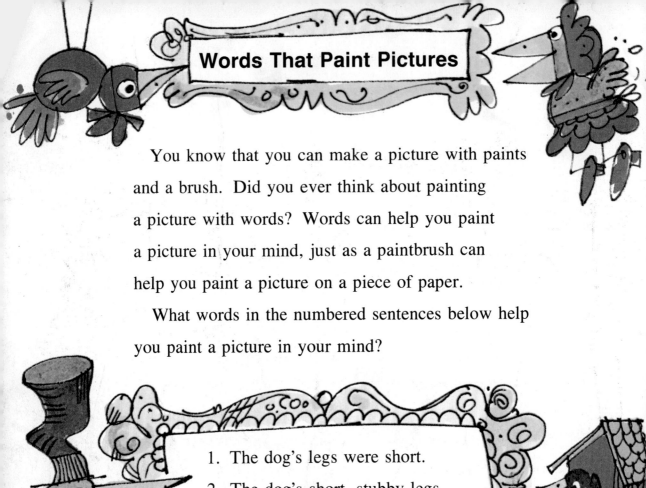

Words That Paint Pictures

You know that you can make a picture with paints and a brush. Did you ever think about painting a picture with words? Words can help you paint a picture in your mind, just as a paintbrush can help you paint a picture on a piece of paper.

What words in the numbered sentences below help you paint a picture in your mind?

1. The dog's legs were short.
2. The dog's short, stubby legs were bent like horseshoes.

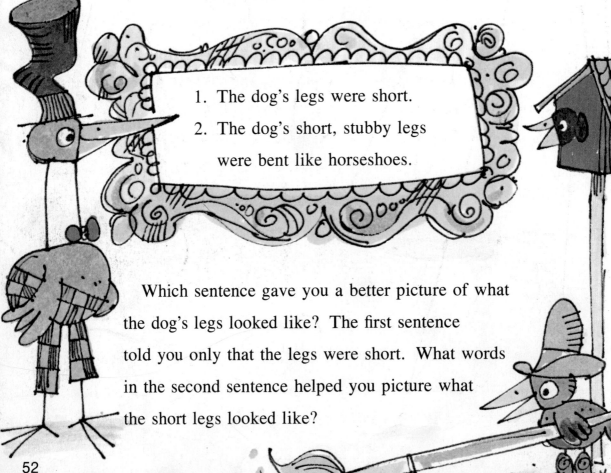

Which sentence gave you a better picture of what the dog's legs looked like? The first sentence told you only that the legs were short. What words in the second sentence helped you picture what the short legs looked like?

What words in the sentences that follow help you paint pictures in your mind?

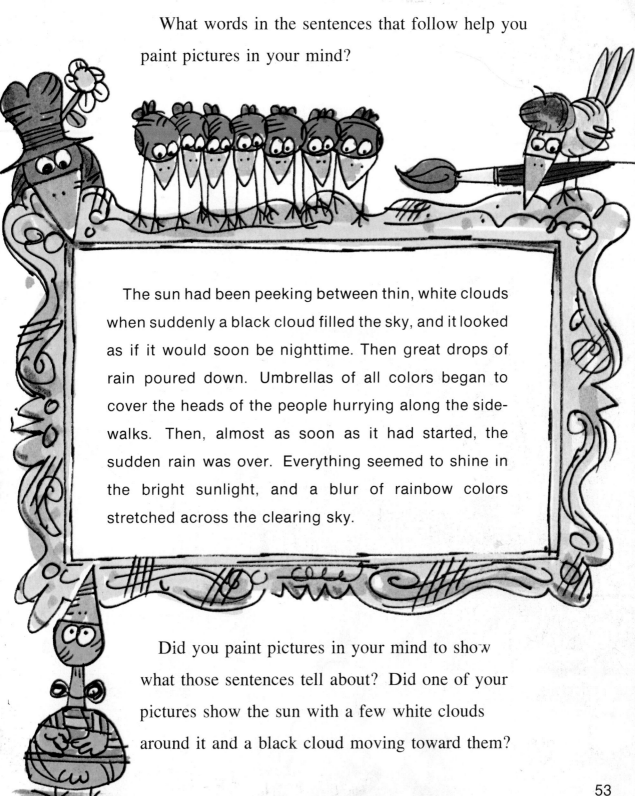

The sun had been peeking between thin, white clouds when suddenly a black cloud filled the sky, and it looked as if it would soon be nighttime. Then great drops of rain poured down. Umbrellas of all colors began to cover the heads of the people hurrying along the sidewalks. Then, almost as soon as it had started, the sudden rain was over. Everything seemed to shine in the bright sunlight, and a blur of rainbow colors stretched across the clearing sky.

Did you paint pictures in your mind to show what those sentences tell about? Did one of your pictures show the sun with a few white clouds around it and a black cloud moving toward them?

Did you make another picture that showed people who were carrying umbrellas of many different colors to keep off the rain?

After the rain was over, the words helped you paint another picture in your mind. Can you tell what the picture looked like?

When you read a story, notice the words that help you picture in your mind what is happening in the story. Doing that will help you understand and enjoy the story.

Rain Poem

The rain was like a little mouse,
quiet, small and gray.
It pattered all around the house
and then it went away.

It did not come, I understand,
indoors at all, until
it found an open window and
left tracks across the sill.

Elizabeth Coatsworth

Reading and Following Directions

When you read directions that you want to follow, you must read very carefully. Could you follow these directions for making a toy airplane?

First, get a clothespin that has a spring on it. Paint the clothespin whatever color you want your airplane to be. After the paint is dry, stick a pipe cleaner or a paper clip through the spring part of the clothespin.

Put a button over each end of the pipe cleaner or paper clip. Then bend back the ends of the cleaner or clip to hold the buttons in place. Now the buttons are the wheels of your airplane.

Next, make a propeller out of paper and put it
on the top of the clothespin, like this:

Then use thin, flat wood or cardboard to make
a long piece with rounded ends, like this:

When you pinch this in the middle between the
tight ends of the clothespin, your airplane will
have its wings.

Your airplane won't fly, but you can push it
along a table-top runway!

Whenever you read directions, try to understand
clearly just what things you are to do and in what
order you are to do them.

DIFFERENT

Hey, hey! I'm just me!

I'm different from anyone else you'll see!

Taller than John — shorter than Sue —

Hair that is darker than Nancy's, too —

Eyes not black, nor really green,

Nor really blue, but in between.

I've got more freckles than Don or Ed,

And I'm not as strong as Billy or Fred.

Jane reads better, but I can add,

And Jim runs faster (which makes me sad!)

Johnny's arms are chocolate brown,

And he's got the happiest grin in town.

Judy's arms are almost white —

And I'm dark tan — and it's all all right,

'Cause Johnny is him, and I am me,

And Judy is Judy, plain to see,

And we're all as different as we can be!

Jo Carr

Once upon a time, and nobody knows when,
so maybe it was just pretend, there was a little
boy with a whistle. He played it ever so much
of the time. He could play "Rory of the Hill"
and lots of other songs.

One very cold day, the little boy was going
outside to play.

"You be sure and stay right close
to the house," his mother said. "You don't
want to get lost, do you?"

"No, Mother," the little boy said.

So off he went outside, dressed
in his warmest clothes — for it was bitter cold.
He had his whistle in his pocket.

He walked around and looked for some snow to make into a snowman, but there wasn't any snow. So he blew into his whistle, but never a sound came out.

"That's strange," said the little boy. "A minute ago, in the house, my whistle was singing away like a bird."

He put it back into his pocket and walked around looking for a stick so he could bang the fence.

He banged the fence with big sticks and with little sticks, but never a sound did they make.

"It's a funny day," the little boy thought,
"with everything so quiet, and so cold and all!
Maybe outside the fence I can find a stick
with some noise in it."

So he stepped outside the gate to look for a
noisy stick, but he didn't find any. He took out
his whistle and blew it as he walked around.
It still didn't make a sound, and still he didn't
find a stick to bang.

He walked around some more. Before
he knew it, he was walking in the little hills
around the house. He blew some more
into his whistle and walked along. One hill
was like another hill. Before he knew it,
the little boy was lost!

BEWARE
of the
BEAR

He stood still and thought. "Seems to me
there's something to do when you're lost,"
he thought. "Let's see. Oh, yes!
You ask a policeman."

So he looked around for a policeman,
but there wasn't any.

The little boy stood still
and thought some more.

"Seems to me there's something
else to do when you're lost,"
he thought. "Let's see. Oh, yes!
You sit right down and wait for somebody
to find you. That way, you don't get lost
more than you already are."

So he sat right down and tooted away
on his whistle which still didn't toot.
He waited and he was glad he was wearing
his warmest clothes, for it was surely
the coldest day of his life. He put
his whistle away in his pocket.
And he put his hands
up his sleeves to keep them warm.

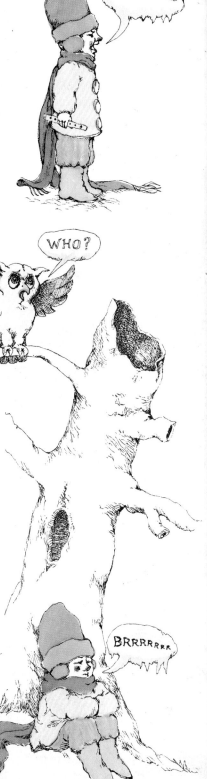

All at once, the clouds came apart, the sun began to shine, and it was a little bit warmer. Suddenly the little boy heard a whistle tooting away, very close to him. He listened.

ONE OF MY

"Why, that's one of *my* songs!" the little boy
said. "Sure, the music I blew must have
frozen. Now the sun is thawing it out!"

He listened, and it sounded very fine, too.
Pretty soon the music stopped.

When it started again, it was a few steps
farther away. It was playing "Rory of the Hill."

"That's another one of my songs!" the little
boy said. "And it's marking the path I walked
along when I was blowing my whistle.
I do believe I can follow my music home!"

He tried, and sure enough he could.
When the music stopped, he waited
until it started again, and he went
where it was.

He had gone a good long way, and he
thought he was almost home, when the music
stopped for a long time. The little boy didn't
know what to think.

Then all at once there was a loud banging
like sticks on a fence.

"The sound of my banging froze, too!" the
little boy said. "And it's thawed out
just in time!"

So he ran ahead and was home in a minute.

He was so happy that he took out his
whistle and started to blow a song. As he
blew it, the sun melted the song he had played
when he first came outside.

His mother opened the door. "Who's playing
those two whistles?"

"It's just me playing a song with myself," the
little boy said.

"Oh," said his mother. "Well, don't go and
get lost, now!"

"No, Mother," said the little boy.
And he didn't.

Do Come for Lunch

Jo Carr

Once upon a time there was a baboon. He was big, and strong, and hairy, and sometimes he was not very kind to the other animals.

One day Baboon asked Stork to come
to his house. "Do come for lunch," he said.

Stork was happy to be asked, and she came.
But when she got near Baboon's house, she saw
that the grass all around had been burned.

"Oh, yes," said Stork to herself. "Some
people do burn off the dead grass. That makes
spring come sooner." And she walked
across the black patch of grass to Baboon's house.
Baboon said, "Come in. It's time to eat."

He and Stork went to a tree-stump table to eat.
On it was one big dish of little sandwiches.

"You first," said Baboon. Stork put
her foot out to the dish to take one
of the little sandwiches.

"Oh, no!" said Baboon. "Look at your foot.
It is all black. You cannot take a sandwich
with that dirty foot! You might get that dirt
on the other sandwiches. Then I would have
to eat a dirty sandwich. Why don't you go down
to the river to wash? Then you can come back."

Stork was sorry about her dirty foot. She
went down to the river to wash the dirt
from her foot. Then she came back.

But she had to walk across the burned grass
again to get to Baboon's house.

Once again Baboon said, "You first." Stork
put out her foot to take a sandwich.

"Oh, no!" said Baboon. "Look at your foot."

Stork looked. Her foot was black with soot
from the burned grass.

Baboon laughed and laughed and laughed.

Stork was sad. She was also angry. Baboon had played a mean trick on her.

So Stork went home to think.

In a few days, Baboon got a letter. It was from Stork. It said:

Baboon said, "She may try to fool me but I am too smart. I will go. I like lunch."

When Baboon got to Stork's house, there was no burned grass. There was only Stork's neat yard and Stork's neat house.

"Come in," said Stork. "It's time to eat. I hope you like blackberries. We are having blackberries for lunch."

Baboon *did* like blackberries best of all.

"Here," said Stork. "You first."

She gave Baboon a tall glass. At the bottom
he could see big juicy blackberries.

Baboon stuck his paw down into the glass,
and grabbed three big ones. But his fist was
too big, and he could not pull it out. Baboon had
to drop the berries before he could take his paw
out of the tall glass.

"My turn," said Stork.

She took the glass. She stuck her long beak
into it. She took out one berry and ate it.
It was very good.

"My, that tasted good," she said.

Then she handed the glass to Baboon.
This time Baboon reached in his paw and
grabbed only two berries. But he could not pull
out his fist, without dropping the berries.

"My turn," said Stork. She ate another big
juicy berry. She handed Baboon the glass.

By this time, Baboon was really angry. He
grabbed only one berry — the biggest one, but
he couldn't get it out. He grabbed another
berry — the smallest one, but even that little
berry would not come out.

Baboon was so angry that he shouted, "Eat your old berries yourself. I don't even like blackberries!"

Stork smiled. "I understand," she said to Baboon. "I had that same feeling about your little sandwiches."

Some Common Beginning Syllables

Many words end with common syllables like <u>ful</u> and <u>ly</u>. There are other common syllables that often come at the beginnings of words.

Look at the words in heavy black letters in these sentences:

1. She put a string of tiny, **round** balls **around** her neck.

2. The **head** of the ax flew off and hit the ground about ten feet **ahead** of him.

3. **Come** see this caterpillar that will someday **become** a butterfly.

4. He ran down that **side** of the street with a dog running **beside** him.

What was done to the first word in heavy black letters in each sentence to make the second?

The letters <u>a</u> and <u>be</u> are very often common syllables at the beginnings of words like <u>ahead</u> and <u>beside</u>. But not always! The letter <u>a</u> in <u>after</u> is not a common syllable. The first syllable in <u>after</u> is <u>af</u>. The <u>be</u> in <u>beak</u> is not a common syllable. The word <u>beak</u> has only one syllable because it has only one vowel sound in it.

82

When you meet new words that begin with <u>a</u> or <u>be</u>, it will often help you find out what those words are if you think the sounds those letters stand for in words like <u>around</u> and <u>become</u>.

Use those sounds now to find out what the words in heavy black letters are in these sentences:

5. He got a gold star as an **award** for jumping higher than anyone else.

6. What **amount** of money would you have if you had five nickels?

7. The poor rabbit found itself **beset** by the hounds.

8. Peanuts grow **beneath** the top of the ground, not above.

Now look at the words in heavy black letters in these sentences:

9. Her **excuse** was that she got so **excited** she forgot to do what she said she would.

10. If you'll **remember,** he got a nice **reward** for finding her lost pocketbook.

Notice that the two words in heavy black letters in Sentence 9 begin with the letters <u>ex</u>. When those two letters come at the beginning of a word, they are always a common syllable and stand for the same sounds they stand for in <u>excuse</u> and <u>excited</u>.

Notice that the two words in heavy black letters in Sentence 10 begin with the letters <u>re</u>. When those two letters come at the beginning of a word, they are very often a common syllable and stand for the same sound they stand for in <u>remember</u> and <u>reward</u>. But not always! In <u>ready</u> and <u>reaching</u>, the letters <u>re</u> are only a part of the first syllable.

When you meet new words that begin with <u>ex</u> or <u>re</u>, it may help you find out what those words are if you think the sounds those letters stand for in <u>excited</u> and <u>reward</u>.

Use those sounds now to help you find out what the words in heavy black letters are in these sentences.

11. My brother **exchanges** stamps with another boy.
12. "Look out for that dog!" she **exclaimed.**
13. Everyone said he could go **except** Tom.
14. When are you going to **return** that book to the library?
15. What kind of marks did you get on your **report** card?
16. How often do you **receive** a letter from her?

SMILES

SMILES

Evan's Corner

by Elizabeth Starr Hill

Evan walked

home from school slowly.

He stopped in front of a pet shop.

In the window, a yellow
bird sang to him from its
golden cage.

"Yellow bird has its own
cage," Evan thought. "*I* want
a place of my own."

He walked on. A bright pink
flower in a window caught his eye.
"Flower has its own pot," he
thought. "Wish *I* had a place
of my own."

He kept going until he reached the big crossing. He waited by the newsstand for the light to change.

"Paper man has his own stand," he thought. "And I, me, myself — I need a place of my own."

He crossed the noisy, busy street and turned into the building where he lived. He climbed up four flights of stairs to the two rooms that he and his family shared.

Soon his three sisters and his two brothers would come home. Then his mother and then his father.

"Mighty lot of family," Evan thought. "And no place to call just *mine*."

Evan had a door key on a string around his neck so he could get in. Almost always he was the first one home. But today the door flew open before he even touched it.

"Surprise!" His mother stood laughing in the doorway. "I was let off from work early. Evan, I beat you home."

Evan gave his mother a big hug. He liked it when she got home ahead of him. Now they could have a talk by themselves before his brothers and sisters came in.

"Mama, you know what I've been wishing for *hard*?" Evan asked.

"Tell me." His mother smiled.

Evan told her the yellow bird had a cage. He told her the flower had a pot. He told her the paper man had a newsstand. He ended, "And *I* want a place of my own."

His mother thought and thought. At first it seemed she might not find a way.

But then her face lighted up. "Why, of course!" she said. "It'll work out just right. There are eight of us. That means each one of us can have a corner!"

Evan jumped to his feet and clapped his hands. "Can I choose mine?"

"Yes." She nodded. "Go ahead. You have first choice, Evan."

Evan ran to every corner of the rooms. One corner had a pretty edge of rug. Some had nothing much. One had a long crack in the wall.

But the one Evan liked best, the one he wanted for his own, had a nice small window and a bit of shiny floor.

"This is mine," Evan said happily. "This is my corner."

Evan's mother had no kitchen. She shared the kitchen down the hall with another lady. Often Evan went with her while she fixed supper.

But that night he didn't. He sat alone and happy on the floor in his corner.

His little brother Adam asked him, "Why you want a corner of your own, Evan?"

Evan thought for a minute. "I want a chance to be lonely," he said finally.

Adam went quietly away.

When supper was ready, Evan's father came to Evan's corner.

"Food's on the table," he said. "You want to eat with us, Evan?"

"Please, Pa," Evan asked, "if I bring my dish here, can I eat by myself?"

"Why, sure," his father said.

So Evan went and got his food and sat down on the floor again.

His family ate at the table in the next room. From his corner, Evan could see them and hear them talking and laughing.

When it was time for dessert, he joined them.

"Why, Evan," said his father, smiling, "I thought you wanted to eat by yourself."

Evan smiled back. "I was lonely," he said.

After supper, there were jobs to do. Evan helped clear the table. He brushed his teeth. He did his homework for school.

When it was done, he sat in his corner again and looked out the window.

The sky was almost dark. Two pigeons cooed sleepily on the window ledge. Stars lighted up, one by one. The breeze blew cooler.

Adam came behind Evan and said softly, "Are you being lonely now, Evan?"

"No," said Evan. "I'm just wasting time. In my own way. In my own corner."

"Can I ever come into your corner?" asked Adam.

"Why don't you pick a corner for your own?" said Evan.

So Adam did. He picked the corner across the room from Evan's. He sat in it. He called, "What shall I do in my corner, Evan?"

"Whatever you like," answered Evan.

But Adam didn't know what to do. After a minute, he left his corner. He played horse with his big sister Lucy. He sat on her back and held onto her pigtails. "Gid-yup, Lucy-horse!" he shouted. They galloped round and round the room.

Evan watched the pigeons fall asleep on the ledge. He watched the sky get darker and the stars get brighter.

Finally his father called, "Come out of your corner, sleepyhead! It's time for bed."

Next morning, as soon as he woke up, Evan ran to his corner. His bit of shiny floor was as bright as ever. His window was still fun to look through.

But Evan felt that his corner needed something more.

What could it be?

He looked at the empty walls. "I know!" he thought suddenly. "I need me a picture! And I'll make it myself!"

In school that morning, Evan painted a picture of the sea. He made big waves and a green boat.

He told his teacher, "I'm going to put this picture up in my own corner."

"That'll be nice," said Miss Gates.

When Evan got home, he hung the picture on the wall beside his window. After he had it good and straight, it looked just right.

Adam came home with their biggest sister, Gloria. She always picked him up at the day-care center on her way home from school.

Adam's eyes lighted up when he saw the picture. "That's mighty pretty, Evan," he said. "Do you think I could make a picture for my corner?"

"Sure you could," said Evan.

Adam ran off. But he couldn't find any paper. He had no crayons. Lucy had, but she was busy with her homework, and he didn't dare speak to her.

He went back to Evan.

Evan was sitting with his back to the room and was looking up at his picture.

Adam asked softly, "Are you being lonely?"

"No."

"Are you wasting time in your own way?"

"No."

"Well, then, what *are* you doing?"

"Enjoying peace and quiet," Evan said.

Adam tiptoed off.

What Evan Needs

That night, Evan didn't sleep well. He lay awake in bed, thinking about his corner.

It had a nice floor and a nice window and a nice picture. But was that enough?

"No," he decided finally. "I need something more. But what?"

He remembered the pink flower in its pot. He thought, "That's it! I need a plant of my own, in my own corner."

On Saturday, Evan went to the playground.
He took his toothbrush glass and a spoon.

The hardtop of the playground was cracked.
Grass and weeds grew up through the cracks.

Evan found a weed with big lacy flowers on it.
He dug it up with his spoon and planted it in his
toothbrush glass.

Then he took it home and put it on the window sill, in his own corner.

Adam came over to see what was going on. "What you doing, Evan?" he asked.

"Watching my plant grow," Evan told him.

"Maybe I'll have a plant, too, someday," Adam said softly.

Evan didn't answer. Something was bothering him.

Even now, his corner seemed not quite perfect. And he didn't know why.

"I got me no desk and no chair," he thought at last. "Why didn't I think of that before?"

Evan skipped off to the grocery store. He asked Mr. Meehan for two old wooden boxes.

"What do you want them for?" Mr. Meehan asked.

"Going to make me a desk and a chair," said Evan, "to put in a place of my own."

Mr. Meehan let him have the boxes.

In his corner, Evan stood one of the boxes up on end. Now it was like a high desk. He turned the other box upside down to make a bench. He sat on the bench.

Surely he had all anyone could wish for. And yet . . .

"How come I feel like something's still missing?" Evan wondered.

He puzzled and puzzled it over. Suddenly he
remembered the yellow bird in its cage.

A great idea struck him. "I know!" he thought.
"I need a pet to take care of. A pet of my own,
in my own corner."

He ran to the pet shop.

He looked at the yellow bird. "Well, yellow
bird," he thought, "you sing fine, but you're not
the pet for me."

He walked into the store. A goldfish swam over to the edge of its bowl and stared at him.

"Afternoon, Mr. Fish," said Evan politely. But he thought, "No sir. That's not the pet for me."

He moved on to the turtle tank. A sign above it read: Turtle with Bowl, Only 50¢!

In the tank, about ten lively baby green turtles swam and scrambled all over each other.

One climbed up on a rock in the middle of the water. It looked at Evan. He felt like laughing. It must have been the funniest turtle in the world!

That baby turtle had a *very* thin neck. Its feet were big and homely. Its eyes were merry and black. If a turtle could smile, that turtle was smiling.

It took a dive off the rock. Clumsy turtle! It landed upside down in the water. Its legs waved wildly in the air.

Evan turned it over very carefully. The turtle winked at him as though it knew a secret. It looked as cheerful as ever.

"Yes, sir! Yes, sir!" Evan told that funny little turtle joyfully. "You're the pet for me."

He asked the pet-shop man, "Please, Mister, do you have a job a boy can do? I'd mighty much like to make enough money to buy me a turtle."

"Sorry, son," said the pet-shop man. "I don't need help. Try next door."

Evan went next door. He crossed the street. He went from store to store, asking for work. He had no luck.

"Maybe some lady would pay me to carry her groceries," thought Evan.

He turned in at the supermarket. He stood just outside the check-out counter. A lady came through. "Carry your bags, lady?" Evan asked.

She didn't answer. She walked right on by.

Evan waited for the next lady. This time he smiled a great big smile and talked a little louder. "Excuse me, but those bags look mighty heavy. Carry them for you?"

"Why, yes." She put them into his arms. "That would be a big help."

Evan carried the groceries up the street to where she lived. The lady thanked him. She gave him a dime.

A dime! He had a dime! Now all he needed was four more.

He raced back to the supermarket. He stood by the check-out. He waited. He smiled. He talked nicely.

Lots of ladies went past. But not one of them wanted him to help her.

Just as Evan began to be afraid he'd never make another cent, a young girl said, "Oh, good! I hate carrying big bags."

She, too, gave Evan a dime.

"Only three more to go," he thought happily.

The next day, the supermarket was closed. But Evan went there right after school on the day after that.

He made one more dime, and then another. He had forty cents!

"Listen, you turtle!" he thought. "You're almost mine now."

But the next day, he fooled around for a while after school. When he finally got to the supermarket, a bigger boy was there ahead of him.

He became very worried. He had supposed it would be so easy to make only one more dime. He stayed around all afternoon, hoping. But the other boy got the jobs. And Evan still had only forty cents.

Next day he ran to the supermarket as fast as his legs would go. Panting, he ran right to the check-out counter. The other boy was not there!

"Hooray!" thought Evan. "Bet this is my lucky day!"

At first things were slow. Then, toward closing time, a great moment came. A white-haired lady said to him, "Sonny, do you think you could help me with these heavy groceries?"

Evan said eagerly, "Yes, *ma'am!*"

Her bag was still on the counter. It was filled clear up to the top. Somehow Evan got his arms around it and lifted it off the counter. "Where to, lady?" he gasped.

"I live just next door," she said sweetly, "but it's three flights up."

Evan stumbled out of the store with the bag. He followed the lady next door without much trouble. But he thought he never *would* get up those stairs.

Yet at last he made it. He eased the bag down onto the lady's kitchen table.

"Thank you," she said. Then she gave him the dime — the wonderful dime — the shining dime that made five!

Evan ran as fast as he could to the pet shop. He poured the dimes on the counter and said proudly, "I made me some money, Mister! I'd like to buy me a turtle."

The pet-shop man counted the dimes. "All right, son. Pick one out," he said.

Evan looked into the tank. His eyes passed from one green turtle to another.

Suddenly he saw a thin neck stretch up from the water. A turtle climbed up the rock — and fell off upside down, on his back.

"This one!" Evan picked the turtle up. "This one is mine!"

Evan carried the turtle home in a small bowl. He put it on top of the upturned wooden box.

Adam was home. He asked excitedly, "What you got now, Evan?"

"My own pet," Evan boasted, "to take care of in my own corner."

Adam wanted to get a closer look at the turtle, but he knew he wasn't supposed to go into Evan's corner.

"Do you think I could ever have a pet of my own?" he asked.

"Sure. When you're much, much older."

Adam went sadly away.

Now Evan had many things.

He had a place of his own. He could be lonely there. He could waste time if he liked. He could enjoy peace and quiet.

He had a fine picture to look at.

He had a bench of his own to sit on, by his own window. His plant was growing tall.

Best of all, he had a pet to love and take care of.

Evan was in his corner whenever he could be. But — it was strange. He still wasn't happy.

"I must need something more," he thought. "But what?"

He asked his sisters. They didn't know.

He asked his brothers. They didn't know either.

His father wasn't home yet. When his mother came home, Evan said, "Mama, I'm not happy in my corner. What do I need now?"

His mother put her head on one side. Together she and Evan stood off from the corner and looked at it. It was beautiful. They both saw that.

"Evan," his mother said finally, "maybe what you need is to leave your corner for a while."

"Why?" Evan asked.

"Well," she said slowly, "just fixing up your own corner isn't enough. Maybe you need to step out now and help somebody else."

Then she left him. He sat alone on his bench, thinking over what she had said.

Adam came in. "Are you enjoying peace and quiet, Evan?" he asked.

"No," said Evan.

"What *are* you doing, then?"

Slowly Evan said, "I'm planning to borrow Lucy's crayons."

"Why?"

"To help you make a picture if you want to. I'm planning to help you fix up your corner so it's just the way you want it. I'm going to help you make it the best, the nicest, the very most wonderful corner in the whole world!"

A big smile spread over Adam's face — and over Evan's face, too.

They ran across the room together to work on Adam's corner.

ICE CREAM TROUBLE

I wish that someone would invent
    A summer ice cream cone;
Some kind that wouldn't drip on me,
    And make poor mother moan.

If there were just a little shelf
    That stuck out all around,
I'm sure I'd get more in myself
    Than on me or the ground!

Jane Lear Talley

THERE ISN'T TIME

There isn't time, there isn't time
To do the things I want to do,
With all the mountain-tops to climb,
And all the woods to wander through,
And all the seas to sail upon,
And everywhere there is to go,
And all the people, every one
Who lives upon the earth, to know.
There's only time, there's only time
To know a few, and do a few,
And then sit down and make a rhyme
About the rest I want to do.

Eleanor Farjeon

JUST LIKE ABRAHAM LINCOLN

by
Bernard
Waber

Mr. Potts, my neighbor,
looks just like
Abraham Lincoln.

Everyone says so.

Everyone says
Mr. Potts has
the biggest ears,
the biggest hands,
the biggest feet,
and the
kindest heart —
just like
Abraham Lincoln.

Everyone says
Mr. Potts has
the saddest eyes —
just like
Abraham Lincoln.
But Mr. Potts
isn't sad.
He isn't sad
one bit.
Mr. Potts
likes to laugh
and tell
funny stories —
just like
Abraham Lincoln.

I like to walk
with Mr. Potts.
We talk and we talk.
We talk about trees.
Trees give us paper
for books.
Trees give us wood
for our tables, and
chairs, and toys.
Trees give us food.

We talk about the sky.
We talk about the sun and the clouds.
We talk about
what causes rain and snow.
We talk about the wind.

We talk about Abraham Lincoln.

Young Abe's home was in the woodlands.

He dressed in buckskin pants and a coonskin cap.

And he ran barefoot through the forest.

Young Abe could hoot like an owl

and hiss like a snake.

We talk and we talk.

Mr. Potts collects things —
things like old letters, pictures,
maps, and a pair of glasses,
all from Lincoln's day.
He even owns a hat and a coat
just like the ones Abraham Lincoln
used to wear.

Mr. Potts reads whenever he has time —
just like Abraham Lincoln.
Abraham Lincoln said,
"The things I want to know are in books."
Mr. Potts told me he said it.

Mr. Potts says,
"The poorest among us
can have books."

Abraham Lincoln was poor.
He walked for miles and miles to borrow a book,
and he walked for miles and miles to return it.

Abe took books to the field
and read while he worked.
At night he read again
by the light of the fire.
In time he read just about
everything there was to read
for fifty miles around
the Lincoln cabin.

On summer evenings, children
come to Mr. Potts's house
and ask to hear stories.

At these times, it is nice
to smell the grass, watch
lightning bugs, and listen
to stories — stories
about Abraham Lincoln.

A Magic Journey

In school our class has been
learning about Abraham Lincoln.
One day Miss Robin, our teacher, said,
"Our class has been picked to give
a program for the school
on Lincoln's birthday.
What do you think we should do?"

"We could tell stories," said one boy.
"We could tell how Abraham Lincoln
was born in a log cabin in Kentucky.
We could tell how Abe didn't
even have a real bed and had
to sleep on a bed of leaves."

129

"We could tell how Abe helped out
with the work," said another boy.
"We could tell how he carried water
from the spring and kept the woodbox full.
And how, as he grew older, he cut down
trees to clear the land for planting."

"We could tell how smart Abe was,"
said a girl. "We could tell how
it wasn't long before he was the
best speller in his class."

"I have an idea," I said to Miss Robin after class,
"but I have to whisper it."

"And why must you whisper?" she asked.

"So it can be a surprise," I answered —
"a wonderful surprise for everyone."
"Very well," she said, "whisper it."

So I whispered it.

Miss Robin smiled.

"That would be a wonderful surprise,"
she said,
"if Mr. Potts is willing."

Mr. Potts was willing.

"You could wear your hat and coat
like Abraham Lincoln's," I said.

Mr. Potts tried on the hat and the coat.
He looked so much like Lincoln, I couldn't
help saying, "If only you had a beard."

"Do you know," said Mr. Potts,
"I've always wanted a good reason for growing a beard."

It has been said that
Abraham Lincoln had
a good reason
for growing a beard.

His reason was a letter
he got from a little girl.
"How handsome you would
look with a beard!"
the little girl wrote.

Abraham Lincoln loved children.
He must have thought it was a good
idea too, for it wasn't
long afterwards that he was wearing
a full-grown beard.

Now Mr. Potts has a beard.
It is black with streaks of gray —
just like Abraham Lincoln's.
People look even more surprised
when they see him.

On the morning of Lincoln's birthday,
Mr. Potts stepped out of his house
and drove away in a hurry.

"Something most surprising
is about to happen," said Miss Robin
later that morning from the school stage.
"Someone has come to take us
on a journey — a magic journey.
He is going to take us back more than a
hundred years to the town of Gettysburg.
It was there that Abraham Lincoln gave
his best known speech. It was
called the Gettysburg Address.
When we get there, we will hear
those very words again."

"Now, in order for the magic to work,"
Miss Robin went on to say,
"everyone must close his eyes
and keep them closed tight.
When we reach Gettysburg, someone
will ask you to open them again.

LISTEN!"

"You may open your eyes now," said
a new voice coming from the stage.
The children opened their eyes and were
surprised at what they saw.

"Welcome to Gettysburg," said a tall
straight man with the face of Abraham Lincoln.

"It's Abraham Lincoln!" cried some.

"It's Mr. Potts," said others who knew him.

Mr. Potts stepped forward on the stage and
began to say the Gettysburg Address —

suddenly, we were in Gettysburg,
over a hundred years ago,
listening to Abraham Lincoln.

He told us never to forget the brave men who
died to keep our country strong and free.
And we won't forget.

We won't forget this day either.

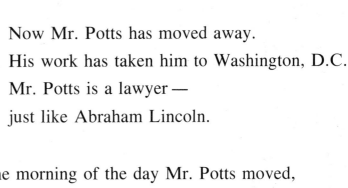

Now Mr. Potts has moved away.
His work has taken him to Washington, D.C.
Mr. Potts is a lawyer —
just like Abraham Lincoln.

On the morning of the day Mr. Potts moved,
I rang his doorbell for the very last time.

"Come in," he said. "I have been waiting for you."

I walked in. Packing boxes were piled everywhere.

"I have something for you," said Mr. Potts.
"I would like you to have this hat," he said,
putting it on my head. The hat was big
and covered my eyes.
"One day it will fit you," said Mr. Potts.
"I would also like you to have this book
about Abraham Lincoln."

Now Mr. Potts is gone. It took a while getting used to
not seeing him on his porch or walking about
with a book under his long arm. It took a while
getting used to the empty house next door.

But the house isn't empty now.
Someone new is moving in.
Someone named Mr. Pettigrew.

I wonder
what he's like.

Washing

What is all this washing about,
Every day, week in, week out?
From getting up till going to bed,
I'm tired of hearing the same thing said.
Whether I'm dirty or whether I'm not.
Whether the water is cold or hot,
Whether I like or whether I don't
Whether I will or whether I won't,
"Have you washed your hands,
and washed your face?"
I seem to live in the washing-place.

John Drinkwater

Every time I climb a tree,

I scrape a leg

Or skin a knee;

And every time I climb a tree,

I find some ants

Or dodge a bee

And get the ants

All over me;

And every time I climb a tree,

"Where have you been?"

They say to me;

But don't they know that I am free

Every time I climb a tree?

EVERY
TIME
I
CLIMB
A TREE

I like it best

To spot a nest

That has an egg

Or maybe three,

And then I skin

The other leg;

But every time I climb a tree,

I see a lot of things to see:

Swallows, rooftops, and TV,

And all the farms and fields there be,

Every time I climb a tree.

Though climbing may be good for ants,

It isn't awfully good for pants,

But, still, it's pretty good for me,

Every time I climb a tree.

David McCord

141

AFTER THE PARTY

Jonathan Blake
Ate too much cake,
He isn't himself today;
He's tucked up in bed
With a feverish head,
And he doesn't much care to play.

Jonathan Blake
Ate too much cake,
And three kinds of ice cream too —
From latest reports
He's quite out of sorts,
And I'm sure the reports are true.

I'm sorry to state
That he also ate
Six pickles, a pie, and a pear;
In fact I confess
It's a reasonable guess
He ate practically everything there.

Yes, Jonathan Blake
Ate too much cake,
So he's not at his best today;
But there's no need for sorrow —
If you come back tomorrow,
I'm sure he'll be out to play.

William Wise

143

Getting Help From Commas

You often see this little mark **,** in a sentence. It's a comma. Commas can help you think how a sentence would sound if you heard someone say it. They can also help you understand clearly what is being said by a sentence.

Suppose a friend of yours said this to you:

1. Mr. Packer said he'd help us.

What if you didn't know who Mr. Packer was? You'd ask, "Who is he?" The answer might be:

2. Mr. Packer is the lawyer next door.

But you wouldn't have had to ask that question if your friend had said this in the first place:

3. Mr. Packer, the lawyer next door, said he'd help us.

Your friend would have stopped for just a second after <u>Packer</u> and after <u>door</u> to let you know that he was telling you who Mr. Packer was. When we write what he said, we put commas in those same places. Those commas tell a reader that what's between them says something extra about someone or something that has just been named. Notice that Sentence 3 puts together all the ideas in Sentences 1 and 2.

144

Now let's suppose that your friend was talking to Mr. Packer instead of to you. Suppose he was telling Mr. Packer that the lawyer next door had said he would help. Your friend might say the same words in the same order. But he wouldn't say them in quite the same way. His voice would be a little higher when he said <u>Packer</u>. He'd stop for a little longer between <u>Packer</u> and <u>the</u>. And he wouldn't stop for even a second after the word <u>door</u>.

Here's how that sentence should look if we wrote it:

4. Mr. Packer, the lawyer next door said he'd help us.

Notice that in both Sentences 3 and 4, each comma tells you to stop for a second. That stopping helps you know how the sentence would sound. Knowing how it would sound helps you understand the sentence. In Sentence 4, the one comma after <u>Packer</u> and no comma after <u>door</u> tell you that Mr. Packer was the one being spoken to.

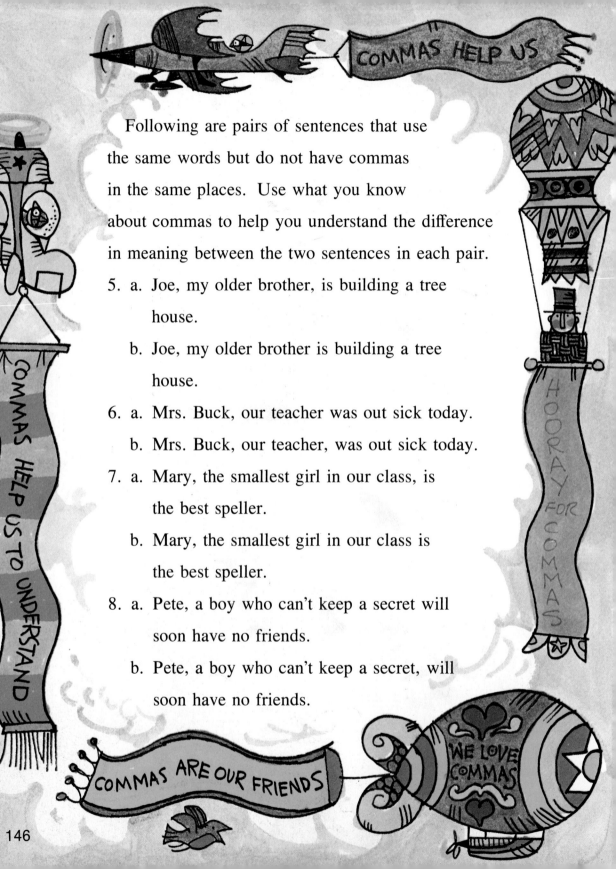

Following are pairs of sentences that use the same words but do not have commas in the same places. Use what you know about commas to help you understand the difference in meaning between the two sentences in each pair.

5. a. Joe, my older brother, is building a tree house.

   b. Joe, my older brother is building a tree house.

6. a. Mrs. Buck, our teacher was out sick today.

   b. Mrs. Buck, our teacher, was out sick today.

7. a. Mary, the smallest girl in our class, is the best speller.

   b. Mary, the smallest girl in our class is the best speller.

8. a. Pete, a boy who can't keep a secret will soon have no friends.

   b. Pete, a boy who can't keep a secret, will soon have no friends.

MR. PICKLEPAW'S POPCORN

By Ruth Adams

Mr. Picklepaw liked to grow things. His backyard was full of the things Mr. Picklepaw liked to grow.

There were giant sunflowers as big as your daddy's head. Oh, much bigger than that.

There were pink and blue flowers running wild all over. Wild as a bag full of stray cats. Oh, much wilder than that.

But mostly there was popcorn.

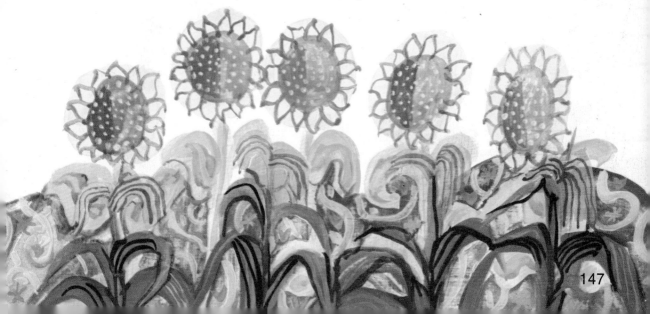

"It looks just like sweet corn growing," said
Mr. Picklepaw looking down the rows of corn.
"But it's much better. Next winter when
the sweet corn is all gone, I can sit by the fire
and pop popcorn. Nothing can beat hot
buttery popcorn."

Then one day it was fall. The green rows
of corn growing in Mr. Picklepaw's backyard
had been slowly, slowly changing color. Now
Mr. Picklepaw saw that the leaves were all
brown.

"Time to pick my popcorn!" he said.

Each little ear, about as long as
Mr. Picklepaw's middle finger, was just right.
The hard golden kernels were packed tight
in shining rows.

The ears rattled one after another
into Mr. Picklepaw's paper bag. Soon the bag
was full. Mr. Picklepaw brought another bag.
Soon that one was full, too. Mr. Picklepaw
filled another and another and another.

He began emptying his bags into baskets.
He filled one basket, then another and
another and another one after that.

When all the popcorn was in the baskets,
Mr. Picklepaw carried them into the shed
at the back of his house. Then he counted
the baskets of popcorn.

"Why," said Mr. Picklepaw, "I have
twenty-nine and a half baskets of popcorn."

The tiny shed was packed tight from floor
to ceiling, from wall to wall, with baskets of corn.

After supper, Mr. Picklepaw went happily
to bed, thinking of his twenty-nine and a half
baskets of popcorn packed in the sheet-iron shed
at the back of his house.

The next morning the sun popped up like
a hot kernel of corn. The day grew warmer and
warmer as days sometimes do in the early fall.
By noon it was hot as a day in July. Oh, much
hotter than that.

"Dear me," said Mr. Picklepaw, "if this keeps
up, I will worry about my popcorn stored
in that iron shed."

He went to take a look at the shed. Hot air was
rising in wiggly wavy lines from the top
of the shed. "I think I will worry a little right now,"
said Mr. Picklepaw. "That shed is almost as hot
as a popcorn popper! But maybe the day will
cool off a little this afternoon."

Mr. Picklepaw looked up at the sky hopefully.
He thought maybe a cloud might come and
cover the sun. But by one o'clock the day was
as hot as hot could be. Oh, much hotter
than that.

"I'd better stop worrying and do something,"
said Mr. Picklepaw. So he went and got
a ladder. Then he turned on the garden hose.
Up the ladder he went carrying the garden
hose with him.

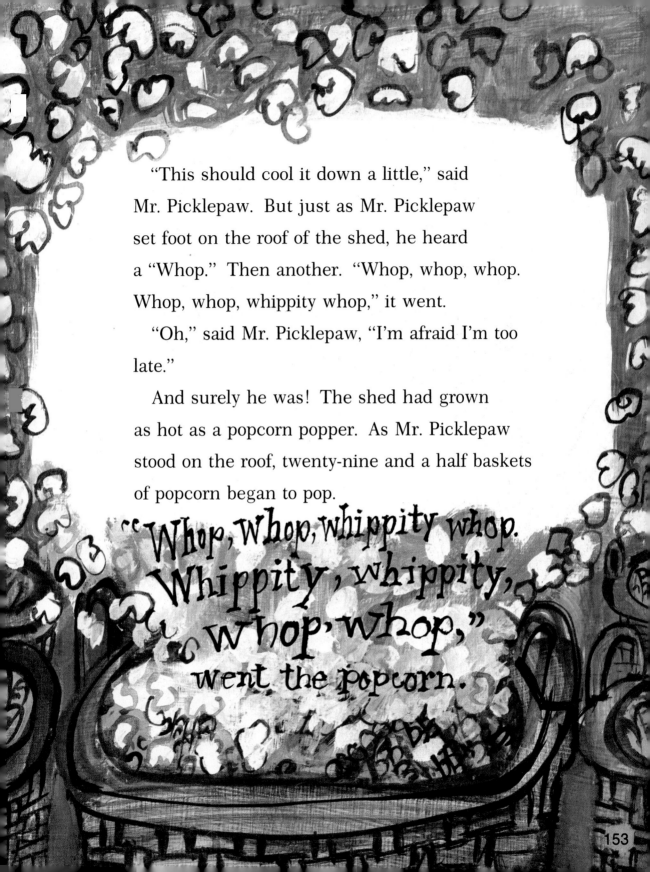

"This should cool it down a little," said
Mr. Picklepaw. But just as Mr. Picklepaw
set foot on the roof of the shed, he heard
a "Whop." Then another. "Whop, whop, whop.
Whop, whop, whippity whop," it went.

"Oh," said Mr. Picklepaw, "I'm afraid I'm too
late."

And surely he was! The shed had grown
as hot as a popcorn popper. As Mr. Picklepaw
stood on the roof, twenty-nine and a half baskets
of popcorn began to pop.

"Whop, whop, whippity whop.
Whippity, whippity,
whop, whop,"
went the popcorn.

As the kernels popped, they began to push
their way over the tops of the baskets. Popcorn
pushed against the roof of the shed. It pushed
and pushed. The roof began to rise. It carried
Mr. Picklepaw with it. Higher and higher it
went. Higher and higher went Mr. Picklepaw.

Up, up, up went the pile of popcorn
with the shed roof on top of it and Mr. Picklepaw
on top of the roof. It went as high as the roof
of the house. Oh, much higher than that.

It went as high as the flagpole in front
of the town hall. Oh, much higher than that.

It went as high as the top of the church.
Oh, much higher than that.

"How in the world am I ever going
to get down?" said Mr. Picklepaw. He peeked
over the edge of the roof. Far below he could see
people running from everywhere looking up
and pointing.

Waiting For A Lift

"I don't suppose they ever saw a mountain of popcorn before," said Mr. Picklepaw proudly.

As he watched, the firemen came with their ladder truck. They began to put up their longest ladder. Up, up, up it came. But it did not come close enough. The fire chief shook his head.

Then the police came. They set up a loud speaker.

"Just sit tight," said the chief of police. "We'll get you down."

"Don't go away," said the mayor.

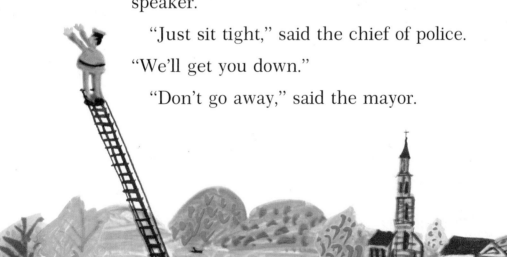

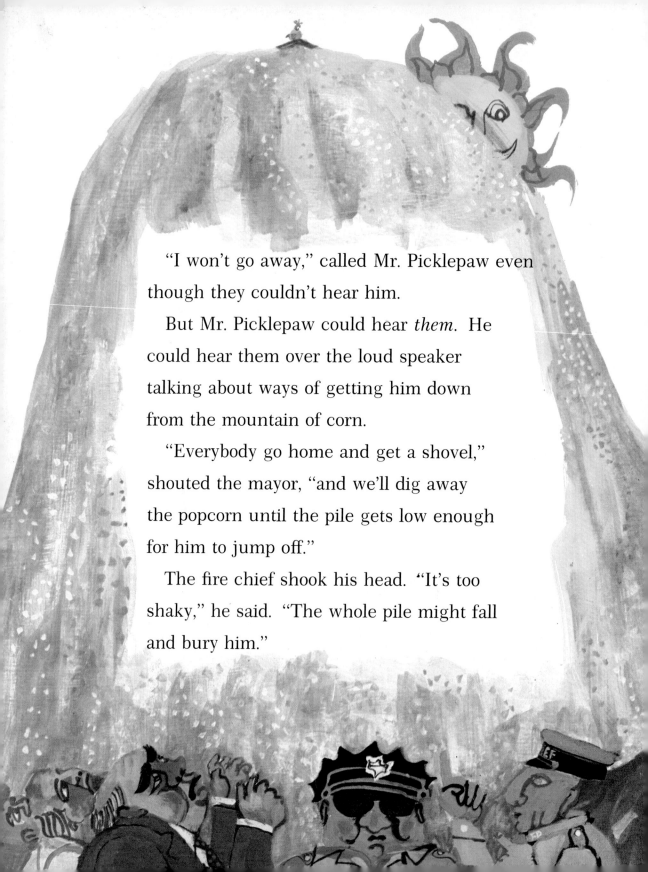

"I won't go away," called Mr. Picklepaw even though they couldn't hear him.

But Mr. Picklepaw could hear *them*. He could hear them over the loud speaker talking about ways of getting him down from the mountain of corn.

"Everybody go home and get a shovel," shouted the mayor, "and we'll dig away the popcorn until the pile gets low enough for him to jump off."

The fire chief shook his head. "It's too shaky," he said. "The whole pile might fall and bury him."

"Maybe he could slide down on that iron roof he's on up there," said the chief of police.

The mayor shook his head. "Too steep," he said. "Why, he'd slide clear into the middle of the next town before we could stop him. Maybe even farther. A man could get hurt doing that."

"Well, I just don't know," said the fire chief. "Looks like he'll have to *eat* his way down."

Just then a little boy who had been jumping up and down excitedly, ran up to the men. "When will the helicopter get here?" he cried.

"Helicopter?" said the mayor. "That's it!"

"Helicopter!" said the fire chief. "Here, Sam, put in a call to the airport," he called to one of his firemen. "Tell them we need a helicopter up here right away."

Half an hour later while the townspeople cheered, a helicopter came and stayed above Mr. Picklepaw on his mountain of popcorn. A ladder was lowered, and Mr. Picklepaw climbed up. He smiled happily.

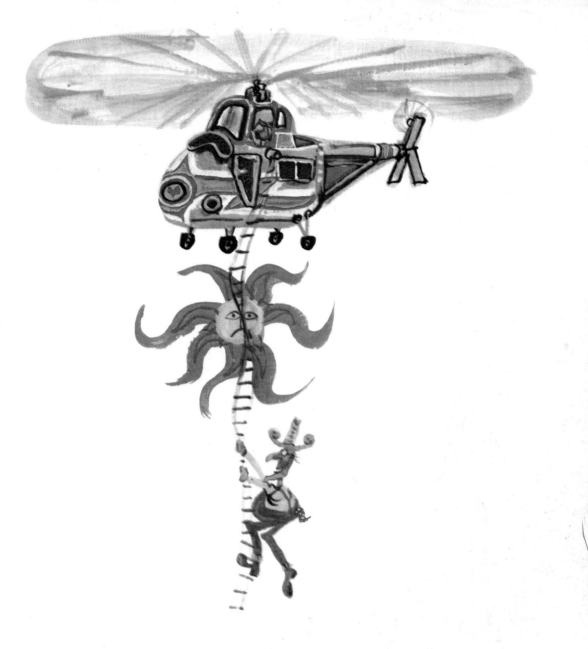

"I always did want to ride in one of these,"
he said.

Mr. Picklepaw looked at the mountain
of popcorn sadly.

"It seems too bad to waste all that lovely corn,"
he said with a sigh.

"Who says it will be wasted?" said the mayor.
"Look at all those children just waiting to go
to it."

Mr. Picklepaw smiled. "Then let them help
themselves and welcome," he said.

So all the children of the town came
with buckets, baskets, and shopping bags.
Each one carried off as much popcorn as he could.
Soon the mountain of popcorn was just a hill.
Then it was a small pile. When the last boy had
filled his basket for the second time,
Mr. Picklepaw found he had enough popcorn
to last him for a week. So he put it away
in paper bags.

That evening in every house in town, mothers
were busy doing things with popcorn. Some
made popcorn balls. Some buttered
the popcorn and salted it. Some mixed peanuts
with it. They all ate and enjoyed it —
to the last fluffy kernel.

Now Mr. Picklepaw still likes to grow things.
His backyard is full of flowers and vegetables.
These are the things Mr. Picklepaw likes to grow.

There are blue-green cabbages as big
as your head. Oh, much bigger than that.

There are beans running up poles as high as
a mountain of popcorn. Well, maybe not quite
as high as that.

But mostly there is popcorn.

And every year, since then, when fall comes
and it is time to pick the popcorn, the children
come with brown paper bags. They pick and
pick and pick with Mr. Picklepaw until there
is enough popcorn to last everybody
through the winter. But they are careful
to keep it in a nice cool place.

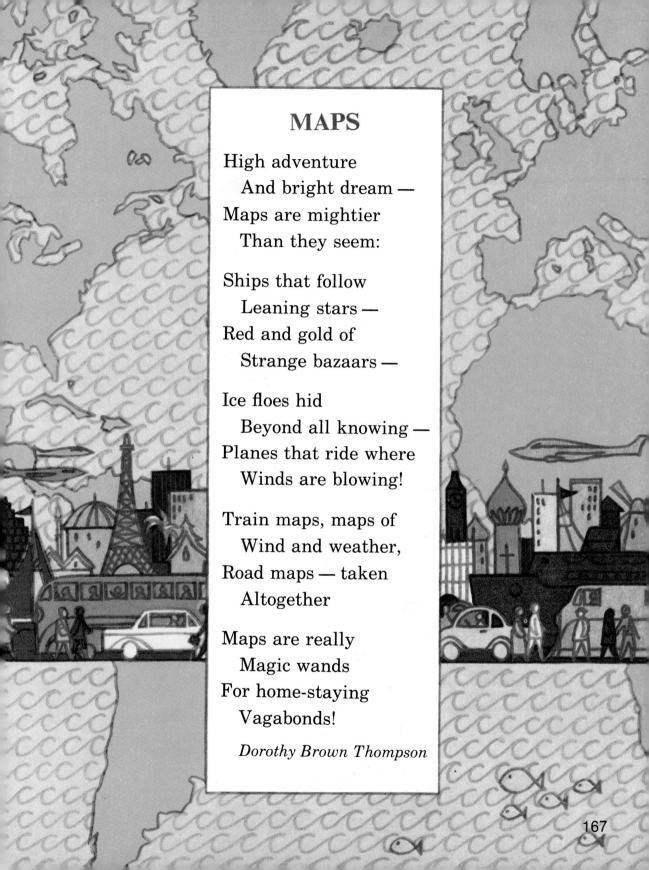

MAPS

High adventure
    And bright dream —
Maps are mightier
    Than they seem:

Ships that follow
    Leaning stars —
Red and gold of
    Strange bazaars —

Ice floes hid
    Beyond all knowing —
Planes that ride where
    Winds are blowing!

Train maps, maps of
    Wind and weather,
Road maps — taken
    Altogether

Maps are really
    Magic wands
For home-staying
    Vagabonds!

Dorothy Brown Thompson

The Quarrel

I quarreled with my brother,
I don't know what about,
One thing led to another
And somehow we fell out.
The start of it was slight,
The end of it was strong,
He said he was right,
I knew he was wrong!

We hated one another.
The afternoon turned black.
Then suddenly my brother
Thumped me on the back,
And said, "Oh, come along!
We can't go on all night —
I was in the wrong."
So he was in the right.

Eleanor Farjeon

Finding Words in Alphabetical Lists

In a telephone book, people's last names are placed so that the first letters in those names come in the same order as they do in the alphabet. They are placed that way so that it will be easy for you to find someone's name quickly.

Sometimes the same thing is done with words. To find quickly a word that is in an alphabetical list, you will need to know the alphabet by heart and how to use it to find the word.

It may help you remember the order in which the letters come in the alphabet if you make a little song out of the alphabet as shown below. Say each heavy black letter and the first syllable of "double-you" a little louder than the rest.

a b **c** d **e** f **g**

h i **j** k **l** m n o **p**

q r **s** t **u** and **v**

w x and **y** and **z**

Suppose you came to the word <u>done</u> when you were looking for <u>hot</u> in an alphabetical list of words. Would you expect to find <u>hot</u> before <u>done</u> or after <u>done</u>? You should, of course, look farther on in the list because <u>h</u> comes after <u>d</u> in the alphabet.

What if you came to a word that began with
the same letter as the word you were trying to find?
Suppose you saw <u>hurry</u> when you were looking for <u>hot</u>.
Now you have to think about the alphabetical order
of the second letters. What are those letters
in <u>hot</u> and <u>hurry</u>? Does <u>o</u> come before or after <u>u</u>
in the alphabet? The word <u>hot</u> should come
before <u>hurry</u>, shouldn't it?

If a word you find begins with the same first two
letters as the one you're looking for, you'll have
to look at the third letters. How do you know
that <u>hot</u> would come after <u>hope</u> but before <u>house</u>?
Why would <u>smell</u> come between <u>school</u> and <u>smile</u>?

Below are five words in heavy black letters.
Following each are five words placed
in alphabetical order. Between which two
of those five words would you expect to find
the word in heavy black letters?

quite	class	love	melt	thin	waste
chief	cabin	clothes	collect	country	cut
sand	sail	salt	same	sat	say
plant	people	pinch	place	play	please
wife	west	which	wild	wind	wish

PICNIC
BY THE
SEA

All that people care about
When they're near the ocean
Is slippery old bottles
Of sun-tan lotion.

Hats and big umbrellas
And how the chairs fold
Is all that seems to matter
On a picnic when you're old.

But I love sunshine
Better than shade,
And sandwiches and doing things
And boats and lemonade.

I'd rather dig tunnels
In the sand than sleep,
Or gather shells and other
Strange treasures to keep

Like driftwood and starfish
And sea-gulls' bones
And pieces of old shipwrecks
And smooth wet stones,

Or just to sit and look and look
At far off things,
The clouds' white waves
And the waves' white wings

And shiverings of silver
A small wind spills
Across the blue harbor,
And far blue hills.

But when you're a grown up
Lady or a man
All that seems to matter
Is the way you tan.

Harry Behn

BEDTIME

Five minutes, five minutes more, please!
    Let me stay five minutes more!
Can't I just finish the castle
    I'm building here on the floor?
Can't I just finish the story
    I'm reading here in my book?
Can't I just finish my bead-chain —
    It *almost* is finished, look!
Can't I just finish this game, please?
    When a game's once begun
It's a pity never to find out
    Whether you've lost or won.
Can't I just stay five minutes?
    Well, can't I stay just four?
Three minutes, then? two minutes?
Can't I stay *one* minute more?

Eleanor Farjeon

Spiders Are Spinners

by Ellsworth Rosen

If you look in a corner

Or under a stair,

You'll see very often

A sticky web there.

You know, without guessing,

A spider has done it,

But do you know why and how it has spun it?

There's more to find out
About spiders than spinning,
And where you should start
Is, of course, the beginning.

Although they're not pretty,

Don't let them alarm you,

For most of the time

No spider will harm you.

They don't like to bite you,

Because you're no treat.

Mosquitoes and beetles are better to eat!

Spiders catch insects
That fly and that crawl;
So spiders, you see,
are your friends after all.

There are all kinds of spiders . . .

Dozens of dozens

Daddy longlegs and crabs

Are some of their cousins.

Why do you think
That most spiders are spinners?
To help them catch insects
For breakfasts and dinners.

Almost always at night, and without any sound,
The spiders will spin out the threads
'Round and 'round.
Their body makes something inside them like milk,
That almost like magic will turn into silk.

The threads keep on coming
As if on a reel,
And sometimes they're stretched
Like the spokes of a wheel.

Try to imagine how strong the threads are.
If they were a rope,
They could pick up a car.

You'll often see bushes with webs like a sheet.

But some webs are messy

And not at all neat.

Some webs are bunched up

In corners of rooms,

And mothers who see them

Will go get their brooms.

The webs are quite sticky;
They're covered with glue,
And bugs that are caught
Can't get out or get through.

The spiders then tie them with threads
Rather neat;
They wrap them like gifts
From their head to their feet.

Spiders can walk on their webs
And don't stick.
Their secret is oil
That makes their feet slick.

The thread of this story

Has spun to the end,

But there's much more to learn

And time you could spend.

To see all you can,

Keep your eyes open wider

Next time you notice a web or a spider.

SOUNDS

MEET MIKI TAKINO

by Helen Copeland

There was going to be a party for the second grade,
with a program about children from other lands.
Miki was picked to be the boy from Japan.
That was fine, the children said, because Miki *was*
a little boy from Japan. He didn't remember
anything about Japan, though.

He lived in New York City above his father's
flower shop.

"And you can ask your grandparents
to the party," the teacher told the second graders.

The children were very happy about this — all but
Miki Takino.

Some of the children said they had four
grandparents. Others had two or three. But Miki had
no grandparents. They had died before he was born.

When Miki got home from school that day, his
mother was sewing. Miki told her about the party,
and she sighed and patted his head.

"Don't worry, Miki. Your father and I will be there. And I know you will be a wonderful little Japanese boy."

He put on his jacket and went down the stairs to the street. He walked toward the East River which wasn't very far away. His friend, Sara, was playing in a little pile of sand behind the fence. She was wearing a yellow sweater, and in the sun her hair was bright gold. Miki sat down beside her.

"Do you have any grandparents?" he asked.

"Oh, yes," she said. "I've got four. Granny Elliot and Gramps and Nonna and Papa T."

"What do they look like?" Miki asked.

"Well Granny Elliot has white hair, Gramps is big and puffs on a pipe, Nonna is a beautiful lady, and Papa T. has a gold watch on a chain."

"Are they coming to the party?" asked Miki.

"Of course," said Sara. "Are yours?"

"Oh, sure!" Miki said. It just slipped out as easy as dreaming.

And before Sara could ask him anything else, he got up and walked away.

He stopped walking when he got around the edge of the bushes. He began to think. Why had he told Sara his grandparents were coming? She would find out the truth at the party. And then how bad he would feel! Not to have grandparents was bad enough — and not telling the truth made it worse.

Miki wished there wasn't going to be any party, so no one would know he didn't have any grandparents.

When he came to the candy store, he stopped
to look in the window. Mrs. Tuttle was busy working
on a little house made of licorice sticks. Mrs. Tuttle
and Miki had been friends ever since the first
day Miki had gone in to buy a licorice stick.

But today Miki didn't have a penny so he was not
going inside. He was just turning away when
Mrs. Tuttle said, "Hello, Miki. Come in and have
some candy."

Mrs. Tuttle was smiling at him. Miki noticed her white hair. He thought maybe Sara's Granny Elliot looked like Mrs. Tuttle.

"Do you know Granny Elliot?" he asked her.

"No," Mrs. Tuttle answered, handing Miki a licorice stick. "Who is Granny Elliot?"

"She's Sara's grandmother, and she has white hair like yours," said Miki. "Sara has two grandmothers and two grandfathers, and they're all coming to our party at school. Grandparents are supposed to come."

"Well! That's nice. I wish my little grandson lived here so I could go to a party at his school," Mrs. Tuttle said.

Miki took a bite of the licorice. Maybe Mrs. Tuttle would come to *his* party! This was such a good idea that he felt like jumping up and down, but instead he asked, "Would you be my grandmother and come to my school party?"

Mrs. Tuttle looked surprised. "Well, I don't know, Miki," she answered. "We'll see."

Mrs. Tuttle's husband, Mr. Tuttle, came
into the store. "I'm going to the bank," he said
to Mrs. Tuttle as he put on his coat. "Hello, Miki.
How are you?"

Miki started to answer, but his eyes were fixed
on the gold chain that Mr. Tuttle was wearing.
"What is that chain for?" he asked.

Mr. Tuttle pulled out a round gold piece. He
put it down close to Miki and the cover popped up
off the face of a watch. "Oh!" Miki exclaimed
happily. He was remembering that Sara's Papa T.
had a gold watch on a chain.

"Mr. Tuttle," he asked excitedly, "are you
a grandfather?"

"Yes, Miki," Mr. Tuttle said. "I'm a grandfather
five times over."

Miki pulled tightly on his licorice stick.
"Mr. Tuttle, would you be *my* grandfather?"

"Now how in the world could I be *your*
grandfather?" Mr. Tuttle laughed. "I'd better
hurry or I'll be late for the bank," he said,
and in another second he was gone.

The excited, happy feeling in Miki had gone, too.

"Thanks for the licorice, Mrs. Tuttle," he said.
"I'll bring you a penny as soon as I can."

Any Grandparents for Miki?

Miki walked home slowly. A little wind blew
off the river and a tugboat was tooting. Miki loved
the sound of a tugboat, but today he didn't even
hear it. All he heard was Mr. Tuttle's big voice
saying, "Now how in the world could I
be *your* grandfather?"

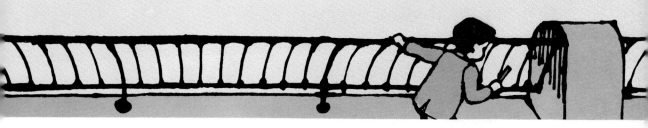

When he got home, Mr. Kelly was there.
Mr. Kelly was the man who came to get
the fluffy dresses that Miki's mother made
for little girls.

"Well, I see you've been eating licorice, young
man," he said.

Miki liked Mr. Kelly's droopy red mustache.
Miki wondered if Mr. Kelly was like Sara's
grandfather, Gramps.

"Mr. Kelly, do you have a pipe?" he asked.

"Well, don't that beat all! Mrs. Kelly says you
can smell it a mile off. I guess it's the truth."

He pulled a pipe out of an inside pocket.
"Here it is, Miki."

"Do you know anybody named Gramps,
Mr. Kelly?" Miki asked.

"Well," Mr. Kelly said, scratching his head. "Sure
I know somebody named Gramps. I've got
a little boy in Texas that calls me Gramps."

Miki's heart was beating hard. "Oh, Mr. Kelly,
could I call you Gramps, too?"

"Why, sure, you can call me Gramps, Miki. I'd
like that."

"I'd like it, too!" said Miki. His eyes were shining.

"And Gramps, oh Gramps," he said, "could you come to our school party tomorrow? Grandparents are supposed to come and I don't have any and Sara has four and I have a costume and we're going to have ice cream . . ."

There was a lot more to say but his mother
stopped him, "Now Miki," she said, "that's enough.
Mr. Kelly is a busy man. How could he come
to your party?"

Mr. Kelly looked at Miki. "Well, now, I don't
know, Mrs. Takino," he said. "I'd like to come . . .
and maybe my wife and her mother would like
to come, too. What time is the party, Miki?"

"Seven o'clock. Will you come, Mr. Kelly?
Will you, Gramps?"

"Maybe, Miki, maybe. Here," he said, handing
Miki a penny. "Go have a licorice on me. Tell
them your Gramps gave it to you."

The door closed behind Mr. Kelly.

Miki flew around the room, waving his arms
like a bird. "He's coming! He's coming! He's
coming!" he sang.

His mother caught him and hugged him tight.
"Miki, don't count on it," she said, and her face was
sad. "Mr. Kelly was just being kind. He did not
want to say *no* to you."

"Yes, he'll come. I know he'll come. And he
gave me a penny." Miki ran from his mother
to the door. "I'll give it to Mrs. Tuttle," he said.

Panting hard from running all the way, Miki put his penny on the counter in front of Mrs. Tuttle.

"Here," he said. "Gramps gave me this penny."

"Oh," Mrs. Tuttle said, "that was nice, but I *gave* you the licorice. You didn't have to bring me a penny."

"I want to, though," Miki said. *"Gramps* gave it to me and I want to give it to you."

"Who gave it to you?"

"Gramps," Miki said again.

"But you said you didn't have any grandparents!"

"Oh, I didn't, but I have one now. He is really Mr. Kelly, but he said I can call him Gramps. And he's coming to our party. Some children have four grandparents, like Sara, but all you really need is one."

Mrs. Tuttle smiled a little as she put the penny away. "What time did you say, Miki?" she asked.

"Tomorrow at seven," he said. "Bye, Mrs. Tuttle."

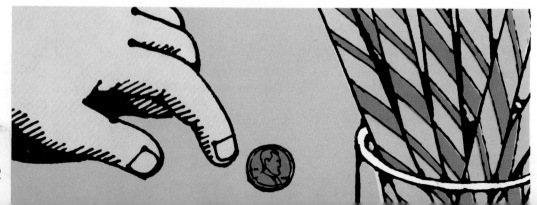

Tomorrow at seven finally came. Up on the stage
were the children in Miki's class, dressed in costumes
of other lands. Miki wondered if Mr. Kelly was out
in front with his mother and father.

Music was playing and the children were lined up
watching their teacher, Miss Prentiss. There was
singing and dancing. Sara was beside Miki. She
was dressed like a Dutch girl. It was so exciting
being on the stage, that Miki almost wished the time
for ice cream would never come.

But soon the program was over. Across the room
he saw his mother. She was wearing a silk dress.
It was the one from Japan that she kept packed
in a sweet-smelling box. Miki's father was standing
beside her.

Then he saw Sara with her mother and father
and her grandparents. He knew Granny Elliott
by her white hair, and big Gramps, and Nonna, who
was a beautiful lady, and Papa T.

Miss Prentiss came over to Miki and took his hand. Her other hand was up, and the talking and laughing stopped. Even grownups know how to be quiet when a teacher puts up her hand.

"I'm happy everyone could come," Miss Prentiss was saying. "I'm happy, too, that so many of the children were able to have their grandparents with them tonight."

Miki's heart sank and he wanted to go over and stand by his mother, but Miss Prentiss still held his hand.

"I've just discovered," she said, "that one of the children has asked five grandparents to our party."

But you can only have four, Miki thought.

Then Miss Prentiss picked Miki up and put him on a chair beside her. "I want you all to meet Miki Takino and his five adopted grandparents," she said.

There was a little movement in the crowd, and here came Mr. Kelly, his big red mustache neatly combed. Miki threw his arms around the big man's neck. "Oh, Gramps," he cried, "you came!" Then he noticed the two ladies with Mr. Kelly.

"I'm Granny Betsy," one of them said, and she
bent down and kissed Miki on the cheek.

"I'm Great Granny," said the other lady.
Someone moved a chair for Great Granny to sit on.

Then Miss Prentiss said, "And here are Miki's two
other adopted grandparents, Mr. and Mrs. Tuttle."

Standing beside Mrs. Tuttle was Mr. Tuttle, wearing his gold watch chain. Mrs. Tuttle was not in her white candy-store dress, but was wearing a pretty blue one. They waved at Miki, and Miki waved back. Then all the people clapped.

Miki had never been so excited. "Oh," he said. It was hardly more than a whisper, but everyone heard it.

Later when the room was filled with voices, the little boy from Japan sat on the floor in a quiet corner with Sara. And as he shared his ice cream with her, he was happily explaining about his five grandparents.

ABOUT THE TEETH OF SHARKS

The thing about a shark is — teeth,
One row above, one row beneath.

Now take a close look. Do you find
It has another row behind?

Still closer — here, I'll hold your hat:
Has it a third row behind that?

Now look in and . . . Look out! Oh my,
I'll never know now! Well, good-by.

John Ciardi

HAWAII

Hawaii is a chain of mountains standing in the sea. These mountains are called islands because of the deep water all around them.

Because Hawaii is made up of islands, its people are always close to the sea.

These mountains are made when pressure and heat build up inside the earth. Then melted rock shoots up through the earth's outer covering.

This jet of fiery rock is a volcano. When the huge pile of hot rock cools, it becomes an island.

Breakers are big waves from the sea which crash into the shore.

Water that cuts away from the sea into the land is called a bay. Even when the sea is choppy, boats are safe in the still water of the bay.

Hawaiians get many important things, like food, from the sea life around them. Many fish, sea turtles, and other animals live nearby in the clear blue water.

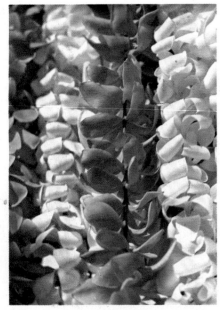

Plants grow well in the soil around volcanos. Hawaii is warm and sunny with more than enough rain.

Many bright flowers of all colors grow well on the islands. The people use these flowers to make the beautiful leis they wear.

The farmers on Hawaii can't grow many of the foods they need. But they do grow a few foods very well, and these are sold to lands across the sea. What food plants do you see growing here?

The roots of the banyan tree grow high in the air. They grow long enough to reach the ground. Then another tree begins to grow in the new place.

Hawaiian children love to swing on the long roots of the banyan tree.

Sliding down long hills on Ti leaves is muddy fun!

Hawaii is called a "melting pot" because its people come from many other countries and all live happily together.

PUNIA AND THE KING OF THE SHARKS

by
BEVERLY
MOHAN

Long ago, in the cold waters of a bay on the island of Hawaii, there lived a great shark called Kai. He was the king of the sharks, and there were ten sharks with him.

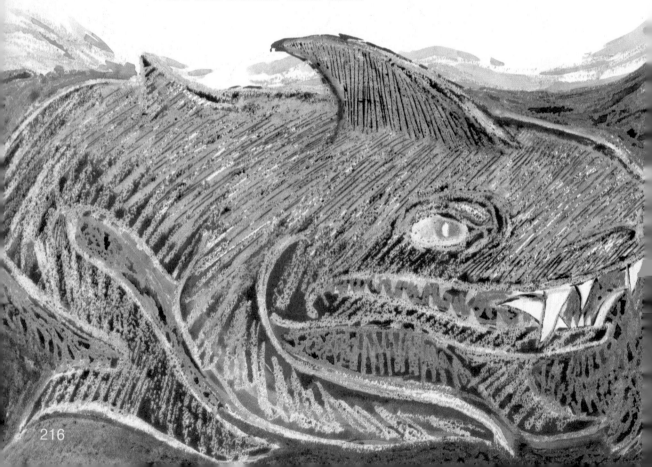

In the bay, among the rocks and waving seaweed, there was a cave full of lobsters. This was where King Kai had his home. When the king was hungry, he just helped himself to a lobster, so the cave was a very good place for him and for the other ten sharks. The only food they liked better than lobster for dinner was a swimmer or a fisherman who was brave enough to come into the bay.

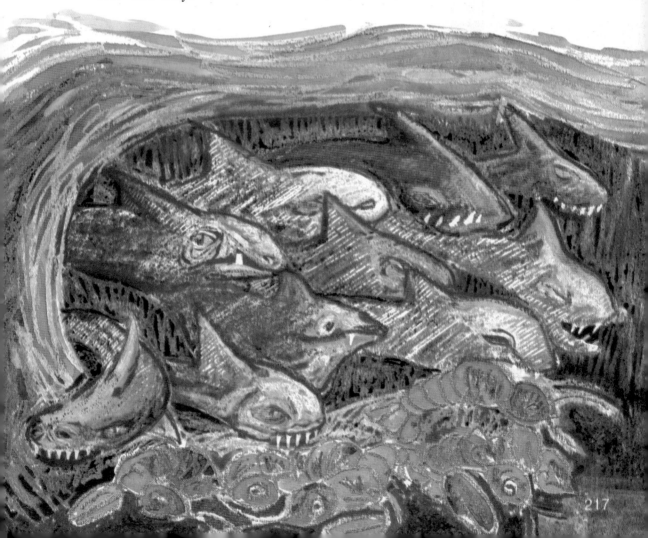

Nearby, on the shore, was the small town of Kohala. Many brave men lived there. Most of them had given up fishing and swimming, for they were not quite brave enough to take the chance of meeting the king of the sharks.

Above King Kai's lobster cave and closest to the shore lived the boy Punia and his mother. They had a garden, and in it, they grew sweet potatoes.

They also grew enough other vegetables to
keep them from being hungry. But often they
wanted something else to eat — a bit of fish or
lobster to go with the vegetables they had every
night for dinner.

At these times, Punia's mother would look at the large iron pot she had used for boiling lobsters when Punia's father was alive. She would say to Punia, "It is a long time since your father was lost at sea. He was the bravest fisherman of all, and was not even afraid of King Kai. The iron pot grows rusty from not being used."

Then she would sigh and say, "How good a bit of lobster would be with our sweet potatoes tonight."

His mother said this very thing every day for a hundred days. So one day, Punia made up his mind to get some lobsters for her.

He walked down by the shore above the cave of the lobsters, and he said to himself, "This King Kai is a mighty shark, but I will find a way to fool him."

As he walked and talked, he stumbled over a rock. Then he smiled, and his eyes lighted up with the idea that came to him.

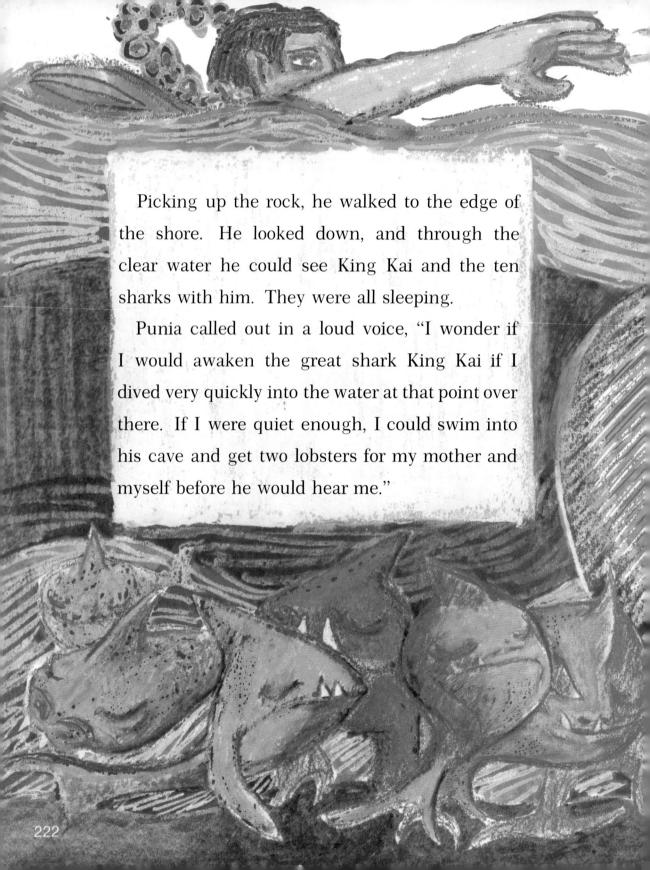

Picking up the rock, he walked to the edge of the shore. He looked down, and through the clear water he could see King Kai and the ten sharks with him. They were all sleeping.

Punia called out in a loud voice, "I wonder if I would awaken the great shark King Kai if I dived very quickly into the water at that point over there. If I were quiet enough, I could swim into his cave and get two lobsters for my mother and myself before he would hear me."

The king of the sharks did not even open his eyes, but he had heard Punia. He whispered to the other sharks, "Let us hurry over to the point where Punia dives and eat him up."

Then Punia threw his rock toward the point. As soon as the rock hit the water, all the sharks dashed away toward the spot. Very quietly, Punia slipped into the water. He swam down into the cave and got two lobsters. In a moment, he was up again and back on the shore.

He called out, "Here is Punia, and he is safe. It was the first shark, the second shark, the third shark, the fourth shark, the fifth shark, the sixth shark, the seventh shark, the eighth shark, the ninth shark — it was the tenth shark, yes, the tenth shark, the one with the thin tail, that showed Punia what to do."

When King Kai heard this, he counted the sharks until he got to the tenth one, the one with the thin tail. He looked at this shark and said angrily, "So, it was you, Thin-tail, that showed the boy Punia what to do. You shall leave this cave and never return, for if you do, I will eat you up."

After a few days, Punia went back to the shore above the cave. He could see the sharks. They were all awake this time. But he called out as before, "I can dive to the place over there where big rocks are, then swim into King Kai's cave. I can get two lobsters for my mother and myself."

Then Punia got ready. He threw a stick to the place where the big rocks were. This time the sharks swam even faster to the place where the stick hit the water.

Again Punia dived down into King Kai's cave and got two lobsters. He swam back to the top, and crawled quickly onto the shore.

Then he called out, "It was the first shark, the second shark, the third shark, the fourth shark, the fifth shark, the sixth shark, the seventh shark, the eighth shark — it was the ninth shark, the one with the very fat stomach, that told Punia what to do."

King Kai was very angry and shouted, "So, it was you, Fat-shark, that told the boy Punia what to do. You shall leave this cave and never return, or I will eat you!"

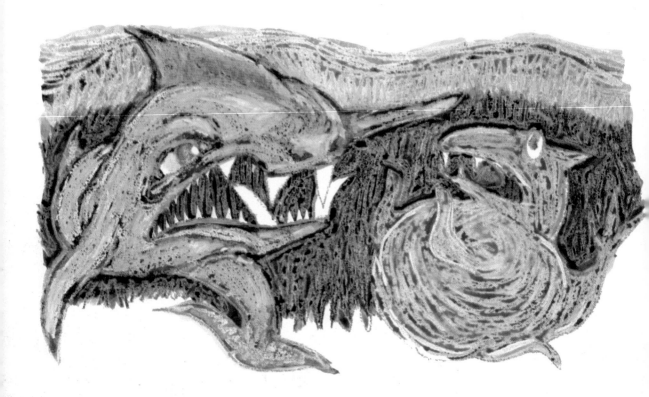

Now Punia, knowing how angry King Kai was at being fooled again, did not go back to the shore above the cave for many days.

Instead he played games with the other boys. He helped his mother fix a hole in the roof of their house, and he did other work.

Punia Meets the King

Then one day, when it seemed a long time since he had smelled the good smell of lobster boiling, he went to the shore above the cave again.

This time Punia called out, "I am very hot. I think I will take a swim. I will see where my father's boat sank in the deep water."

King Kai knew well the place Punia was talking about. He said quietly to the other sharks, "Come, let us go to the boat and be ready this time to catch this foolish boy when he gets there."

All the sharks slipped quietly out of the cave toward the boat, which was quite far away.

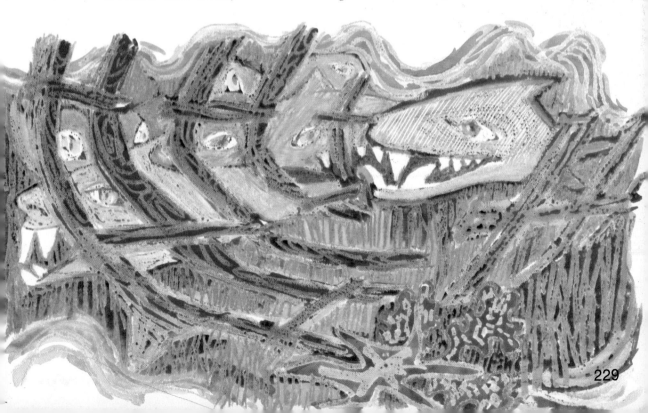

This time Punia had time to bring up more than two lobsters. He got enough for his mother to have some left over for another time.

When King Kai returned to his cave, he was terribly angry. He had waited a long time at the boat, but Punia had not come. Then he heard the voice of Punia, and his anger was even greater than before.

Punia was saying, "It was the first shark, the second shark, the third shark, the fourth shark, the fifth shark, the sixth shark, the seventh shark — it was the eighth shark, the one with the dark scar on his tail, that told Punia what to do."

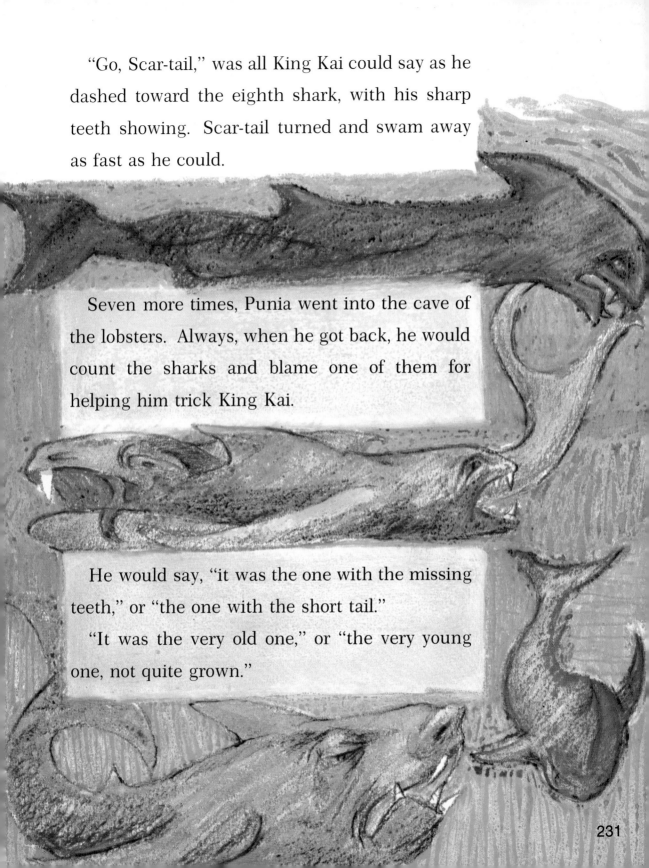

"Go, Scar-tail," was all King Kai could say as he dashed toward the eighth shark, with his sharp teeth showing. Scar-tail turned and swam away as fast as he could.

Seven more times, Punia went into the cave of the lobsters. Always, when he got back, he would count the sharks and blame one of them for helping him trick King Kai.

He would say, "it was the one with the missing teeth," or "the one with the short tail."

"It was the very old one," or "the very young one, not quite grown."

"It was the one with the red eyes," or "the one with the wrinkles in his nose."

And each time, King Kai would say, "So, it was you that showed the boy Punia what to do. Leave this cave and never return, or I shall eat you."

At last, the day came when all ten sharks were gone, and King Kai was all alone.

Soon after this day, Punia went into the forest. He cut down two large pieces of strong wood. Then he got two shorter sticks to use in lighting a fire. These sticks were called fire sticks because when rubbed together, they heated quickly and were used to start fires. Punia also got some charcoal and some food to eat.

All these things Punia put into a bag, and he carried the bag to the shore. When he got there, he called out once again in a loud voice, "If I dive now, and if King Kai bites me, my mother will hear my cries and come and save me. But if the king takes me into his mouth whole, I shall die and never come back again."

Hearing this, King Kai said to himself, "So, at last I will get you, Punia. I will be careful not to bite you. I will take you into my mouth whole and swallow you in one piece. Then you will die and never come back again. This time I will get you!"

Then Punia, holding tightly to his bag, jumped into the water. King Kai opened his mouth very wide, and Punia stepped inside. Quickly Punia took the two large pieces of strong wood out of his bag. He put them between King Kai's jaws so the shark-king could not close his mouth. King Kai was angry, and he went dashing and splashing through the water.

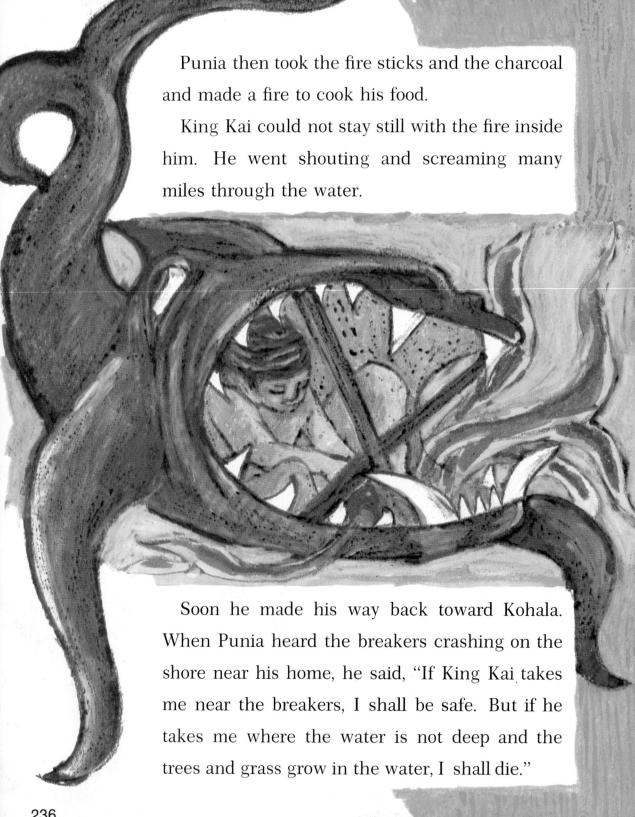

Punia then took the fire sticks and the charcoal and made a fire to cook his food.

King Kai could not stay still with the fire inside him. He went shouting and screaming many miles through the water.

Soon he made his way back toward Kohala. When Punia heard the breakers crashing on the shore near his home, he said, "If King Kai takes me near the breakers, I shall be safe. But if he takes me where the water is not deep and the trees and grass grow in the water, I shall die."

When King Kai heard this, he quickly swam toward the place where the trees and grass grew in the water. But when he got there, he could not get out again. The water was not very deep, and the trees and grass were in his way.

Seeing that King Kai was stuck, Punia quickly jumped out of the shark-king's mouth and shouted, "See who has come to visit us. It is the mighty King Kai that I have trapped at last!"

Hearing this, the men ran from their homes
down to the shore. They pulled King Kai out of
the water onto the sand. And that was the end of
the terrible shark-king.

From that day on, there were no longer any sharks around the cave of the lobsters. Punia's mother's cooking pot was no longer rusty from not being used. And it was all because of the brave boy Punia, who had fooled King Kai, the mighty king of the sharks.

More Help From Commas

You know that commas can help you understand what you're reading if you stop for just a moment whenever you come to one. You know from the commas that Sentences 1 and 2 below do not have the same meaning:

1. Mr. Hunter, our postman likes to fish.
2. Mr. Hunter, our postman, likes to fish.

Let's look at another way in which commas can help you understand what you read. Try to read this sentence:

3. For lunch we had chicken soup pork sausage honey bread butter beans squash pie and chocolate milk.

How many different foods were there at that lunch? Did they have chicken and soup, or did they have chicken soup? Did they have honey and bread and butter and beans, or did they have a kind of bread called honey bread and a kind of beans called butter beans? You can't tell just what they had because commas were not put into that sentence to show where the reader should stop for a moment. In Sentences 4 and 5 below, commas have been put into that sentence so that the same words say things that are not the same.

4. For lunch we had chicken, soup, pork, sausage, honey, bread, butter, beans, squash, pie, and chocolate milk.

5. For lunch we had chicken soup, pork sausage, honey bread, butter beans, squash pie, and chocolate milk.

In Sentence 4, how many different foods were named? How many in Sentence 5?

When you come to a list of things in your reading, notice the commas and use them to help you know exactly what the different things are.

Following are pairs of sentences that use the same words but have commas in different places. Use what you know about commas to help you understand the difference in meaning between the two sentences in each pair.

6. a. The animals I found most fun to watch at the zoo were the leopard, frog, elephant, seal, alligator, turtle, and kangaroo rat.

   b. The animals I found most fun to watch at the zoo were the leopard frog, elephant seal, alligator turtle, and kangaroo rat.

7. a. Margaret, Anne, Mary, Louise, Betty, Jo, and Susan are all coming to the party.

   b. Margaret Anne, Mary Louise, Betty Jo, and Susan are all coming to the party.

8. a. To wrap all these gifts, we'll need cardboard, boxes, heavy foil, paper, ribbon, tape, silk, yarn, wire, rope, and thread.

   b. To wrap all these gifts, we'll need cardboard boxes, heavy foil paper, ribbon tape, silk yarn, wire rope, and thread.

9. a. The colors I like best are rust, red, cream white, dandelion yellow, blue, black, flamingo pink, and green.

   b. The colors I like best are rust red, cream, white, dandelion yellow, blue black, flamingo, pink, and green.

10. a. Today I saw a pigeon, hawk, tiger, moth, wolf, spider, grasshopper, mouse, and barn swallow.

    b. Today I saw a pigeon hawk, tiger moth, wolf spider, grasshopper mouse, and barn swallow.

Poor old Jonathan Bing
Went out in his carriage to visit the King,
But everyone pointed and said, "Look at that!
Jonathan Bing has forgotten his hat!"
(He'd forgotten his hat!)

Poor old Jonathan Bing
Went home and put on a new hat for the King,
But up by the palace a soldier said, "Hi!
You can't see the king; you've forgotten your tie!"
(He'd forgotten his tie!)

Poor old Jonathan Bing,

He put on a *beautiful* tie for the King,

But when he arrived an Archbishop said, "Ho!

You can't come to court in pajamas, you know!"

Poor old Jonathan Bing

Went home and addressed a short note to the King:

If you please will excuse me

I won't come to tea;

For home's the best place for

All people like me!

Beatrice Curtis Brown

Anyone Could, But
by Bernice Wells Carlson

People in the Play

LORD CHAMBERLAIN   TWO WOMEN

KING *Micheal*   TWO MEN

TWO SHEPHERDS   GREG

Place: A road. A stone is in the middle of the road. The Lord Chamberlain and the King stand on either side of the stone.

LORD CHAMBERLAIN: Your Highness, I do not understand. Why did you dig a hole in the road? You put a pot of gold in the hole. And then you put this huge stone over the gold! The stone is in the way.

KING: Yes, it is. But this stone may help me find a man.

246

LORD CHAMBERLAIN: Your Highness, you'll
never catch a thief this way. He'll never look
for gold down there.

KING: I'm not looking for a thief. I don't think
anyone will find the gold down there.
But someone may.

LORD CHAMBERLAIN: Your Highness, are you
feeling well? Is your head all right?
What is the matter?

KING: Don't worry, Lord Chamberlain.
My head is well. My heart is heavy.
You see, I am worried
about my people.

LORD CHAMBERLAIN: I can understand that.

They depend on you for everything.

KING: That's just the trouble. They

depend upon me too much.

I think they have forgotten

how to help themselves.

I think they have forgotten how to help

one another.

LORD CHAMBERLAIN: But what good is a stone

in the road?

KING: You'll see. Shh! Here come

two shepherds. Let's hide.

(*They leave.*)

FIRST SHEPHERD: Just look at that! A stone in the road!

SECOND SHEPHERD: Of all things! Thank goodness it wasn't there this morning!

FIRST SHEPHERD: That's right. The sheep would have had to go around.

SECOND SHEPHERD: I hope someone tells the king about this.

FIRST SHEPHERD: I hope he gets it out of the way, and fast!

(*Shepherds leave. King and Lord Chamberlain come back.*)

KING: See what I mean?

LORD CHAMBERLAIN: I think so. Shh! Here come two women.

(*Lord Chamberlain and King leave.*)

FIRST WOMAN: Well, look at that!

SECOND WOMAN: What a terrible stone in the road!

FIRST WOMAN: I'm glad it isn't dark. I might have stumbled on it.

SECOND WOMAN: You might do worse than that. What is this world coming to? A stone in the road! Where is the king?

(*Women leave.*)

FIRST MAN: (*Coming in with Second Man.*) Yes,
business was good, very good. Look!
What is this? A stone in the road.

SECOND MAN: Something should be done
at once!

FIRST MAN: That stone will get in people's way
and hurt our business.

SECOND MAN: I wonder if the king knows
about this.

FIRST MAN: The king must be slipping,
letting a stone stay in the middle
of the road.

(*Men leave.*)

GREG: (*Coming in whistling.*) Look at that stone! Right in the middle of the road. Lucky I saw it before it got dark. Someone might have bumped into it and been hurt. Wonder if I can move it. Let's see. If I push here, it will roll down there. Nothing's in the way. (*Pushes stone.*) There! There she rolls.

What's in the hole? Gold! It must be
the king's gold. No one else has that much
gold! Wonder if someone stole it?
I must tell the king. What will
I do? I can't carry it all. I must get help.

KING: (*Coming in.*) Wait, lad. I've been
looking for you.

GREG: Oh, Your Highness, I just found
this gold. I didn't steal it. Really,
I didn't. There was a stone here. I
rolled it away. Believe me, sir!

KING: I believe you, lad, because I saw
it all. I planned it all.

GREG: You planned it all?

KING: Yes, I have been looking for someone
in my land who thinks of others.
I have been looking for someone
who can do things for himself.
I waited all day, lad. But at last
I found you.

GREG: All day, sir? Why, anyone
could move that stone.

KING: Anyone could do it,
but only you did do it.
Thank you, lad. This gold
is yours.

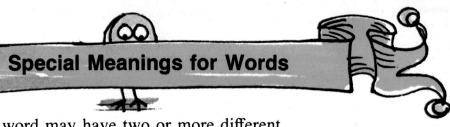

Special Meanings for Words

A word may have two or more different meanings. The meaning it has depends on how it is being used with other words. What are the two different meanings that the word <u>steal</u> has in these two sentences?

1. If you leave your pocketbook there, someone might **steal** it.
2. The game is so close that if Joe ever gets to third base he's almost sure to try to **steal** home.

Sometimes a pair of words or a group of words is used with a special meaning that is quite different from the meaning you might expect. To find out the meaning of such a pair or group of words, you must do the same thing you did with the one word <u>steal</u>. You must think what meaning would make sense with the other words.

Sometimes you will need to use more than just the other words in the same sentence. You may have to think what has been said in an earlier sentence. You may, once in a while, have to look ahead and see what is being said in a sentence that comes later.

Read Sentence 1 below and think about the group of words in heavy black letters:

1. John's been known to tell people things that are not exactly true, so you'd better take anything he says **with a grain of salt.**

That seems to be telling someone to put a tiny piece of salt on anything John says. But you couldn't put salt on someone's talking, could you? And even if you could, it wouldn't make any real sense with the other words in that sentence, would it?

Think what the rest of the sentence is saying. What do those other words lead you to think the speaker is probably telling someone to do? He's probably trying to tell someone not to believe everything John says, isn't he? Those other words help you to know that "take with a grain of salt" means "don't believe you're hearing the exact truth."

Use the other words in each of the following sentences to help you decide what the group of words in heavy black letters means:

2. When Mary got home an hour late for the third day in a row, her mother really **laid down the law to her.**

3. Paul is so much smarter than the rest of us that he **walked off with** the arithmetic prize.

4. There's nothing he enjoys as much as fooling someone, so watch out that he doesn't **slip one over on you.**

5. When Mother took the meat out and tested it, she found that it was done **to a turn.**

6. This will be the first time your Uncle Bill has seen you, so try to **put your best foot forward.**

7. If anything happens to Bob so that he can't play, our team's chances of winning will have come to **a pretty pass.**

8. We all wanted Susan to sing for the parents on "Back-to-School" night, but she said she wouldn't do it **for love or money.**

9. When her pet rabbit escaped from the pen for the tenth time, Pat was **fed up to the eye teeth.**

10. We aren't **getting to first base** on plans for the class party.

11. Tom and Alice **put their heads together** and came up with a new idea.

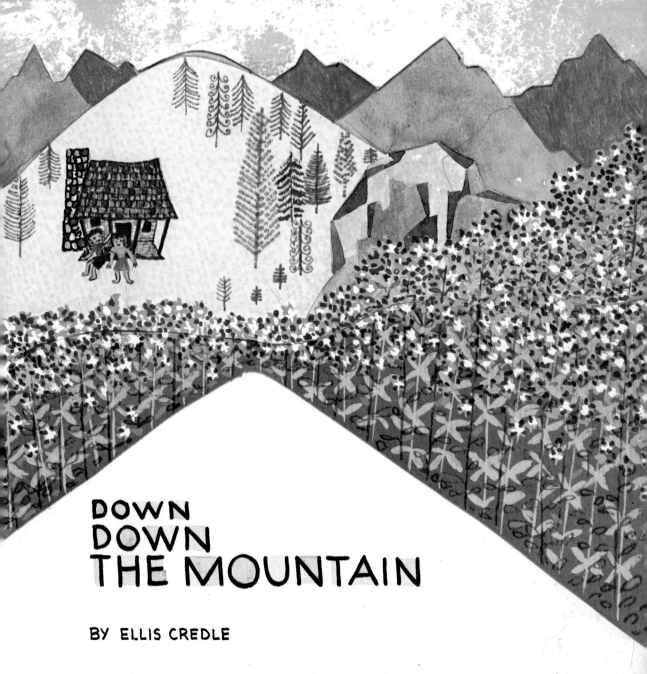

DOWN
DOWN
THE MOUNTAIN

BY ELLIS CREDLE

Once upon a time, in a little log cabin up in the
Blue Ridge Mountains, there lived a little girl
named Hetty and her brother Hank.

Although their home was a small one, it was a cozy place to live. There was a big stone fireplace at one end. That was where Mammy cooked beans and pork in a big black pot. In the middle of the room, there was a long table made of boards. That was where Mammy and Pappy and Hetty and Hank ate their dinner every day.

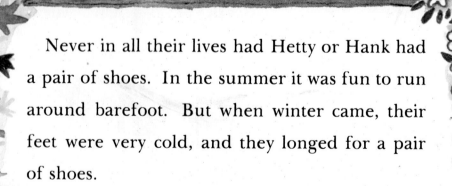

Never in all their lives had Hetty or Hank had a pair of shoes. In the summer it was fun to run around barefoot. But when winter came, their feet were very cold, and they longed for a pair of shoes.

They each wanted a beautiful shining pair that sang, "Creaky-squeaky-creaky-squeaky," every time they walked.

They begged their Mammy to buy them some shoes. She said, "You can't find shoes like that in these hills! Such shining shoes come from the town, away down down the mountain."

So they asked their Pappy, but he said, "There's not a cent of money in this house. We've everything we need right in these hills."

Hetty and Hank felt very sad, but they did not give up.

"Let's ask our Granny," said Hetty. And they did.

"Some shining shoes?" asked Granny. "I'll tell you how you can get them yourselves."

"How? How?" cried Hetty and Hank.

"Plant some turnip seeds," said Granny. "When they have grown into fine big turnips, you can take them down to town. You can trade them for some shining, creaky-squeaky shoes."

"Thanks, Granny. That's what we'll do," cried Hetty and Hank.

They raced away and planted some turnip
seeds right next to Pappy's corn field. Then they
went home singing.

When Hetty and Hank got home, it was dark.
Mammy was waiting for them. She gave them a
nice supper. Then they went to bed. They
dreamed all night about shining shoes that
played a creaky, squeaky song.

The next day they climbed up the steep, steep
mountainside to see if the turnip seeds had come
up. But they had not. Hetty and Hank had to
wait and wait and wait before the baby turnip
leaves peeped out of the ground.

Then there was plenty of work for Hetty and
Hank! They had to pull the weeds each day, and
chase away the worms, the bugs, and the grass-
hoppers that came for a taste of nice green turnip
leaves.

When there was no rain, Hetty and Hank had to bring big buckets of water to make the turnip plants green again.

The little turnips grew and grew until they were the finest and the biggest turnips anywhere in the hill country.

Then Hetty and Hank brought Granny and Mammy and Pappy up to see them.

"Sakes alive!" cried Mammy. "I never saw such big turnips!"

"Yes, sir!" smiled Granny. "These are nice juicy turnips."

"And they'll get a fine price in the town," said Pappy. "Hetty and Hank may have the old gray horse to take them down the mountain."

So Hank quickly brought the gray horse. Then they pulled up all the beautiful turnips and packed them into a big bag.

Pappy put the bag proudly across the gray horse's back. Then he helped Hetty and Hank up onto the horse. Now they were ready to go.

"Good-by!" cried Granny and Mammy and Pappy.

"Good-by!" waved Hetty and Hank. And away they went, clippety, cloppety, down the road to town.

DOWN THE MOUNTAIN

They had not gone very far when they came
to an old man.

"Howdy, young ones!" he called. "What have
you in that big bag?"

"Some turnips we're taking to be sold in the
town," said Hank proudly.

"Oh, my! Turnips!" cried the old man. "How
I'd love some nice juicy turnips for my dinner.
Could you give me just a few?"

"I suppose we wouldn't miss just a few," said
Hetty, and she gave him some.

They rode on. After a while, they came to an old woman who was making soup in a big black pot.

"Howdy, children!" she called. "What have you in that big bag?"

"Some turnips we're taking down to town," said Hank.

"Turnips!" cried the old woman. "Goodness me! How I'd love just a taste of turnip for my dinner. Couldn't you give me just two, for my husband and me?"

"I suppose we wouldn't miss
just two," said Hetty,
and she gave the old woman
two big ones.

Down, down, down they went between the
rows of tall blue mountains — down, down, down
until they came to a little stream.

There the little road ended.

Just then along came a woman on horseback, splashing right down the middle of the stream.

"What's the matter, young ones?" she called.

"We've lost the little road to town," said Hank.

"Follow the stream," said the woman. "That's all the road there is in these parts."

So Hetty and Hank went splashing along and along. Pretty soon they saw the little road going up from the water.

They said good-by to the kind woman and gave her a bunch of turnips for her dinner.

After a while, they came to a man who was taking some turkeys down to town.

"Howdy," said the man. "What have you in that big bag?"

"Some turnips we're taking to sell in the town," said Hank.

"Turnips!" said the man. "I've had nothing to eat since sunup. A nice juicy turnip would sure taste mighty good now."

"We'll have to give him some of the turnips," said Hetty. And they did.

"Thank you, thank you," said the man. "You're good and kind young ones!"

Now they were very near to town. They could look down and see the rooftops in the valley. As the little road became smooth and straight, the gray horse broke into a gallop.

"Here's the town!" cried Hank.

Along they went, clippety clop, clippety clop, past the schoolhouse and past the little red store.

"Whoa!" cried Hank. "Here's the place to trade our turnips for some shining shoes!"

They climbed down and lifted off the bag. Somehow it felt very light and very empty. Had they given all their turnips away?

Hetty put her hand into the bag and brought out one large, fat, lonesome turnip. It was the only one left.

And there shining through the store window were those beautiful, creaky, squeaky, shining shoes!

Hetty and Hank looked at them longingly. But one turnip would not buy a pair of shoes.

Two big tears began to roll down Hetty's cheeks.

"There! There," said Hank. "No use crying. We'll just walk around and see the town. Come on."

So they walked along the little road looking this way and that way. Along and along they went. After a while, they came to a field where there were many, many people. A big sign over the gate said "COUNTRY FAIR."

Hetty and Hank went hustling and bustling about in the crowd. Soon they came to a long row of tables with vegetables on them.

"Oh, here are some turnips!" cried Hetty.

"Are they as big as ours?" asked Hank.

Hetty held up her turnip. It seemed larger and juicier than the rest.

"Howdy, young ones," said the old man who was looking at the turnips. "Do you want to leave that turnip here for the contest?"

"What contest?" asked Hank.

"Why, there's a prize for the finest turnip at the fair," said the old man.

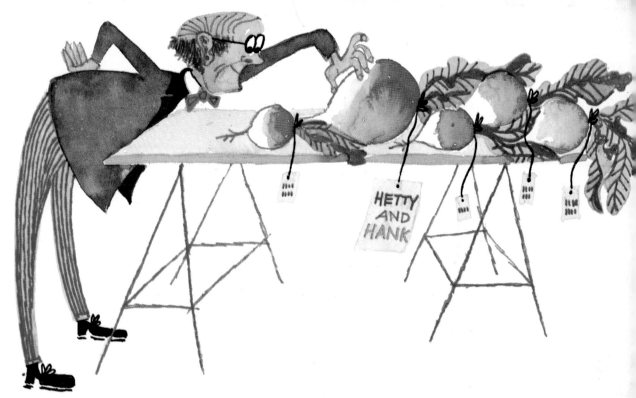

"Let's try it," said Hetty.

"Yes, let's," said Hank.

So the old man put their names on a card and tied it to the fat turnip. Then he put it carefully with the other turnips.

"You're just in time," he said. "I was just getting ready to judge the turnips."

He began to look carefully at the turnips. He felt each one to see how hard it was. When he had tried them all, he held one large turnip high above his head.

"Friends!" he cried. "Here's the finest turnip
at the fair. It belongs to a little girl and a little
boy!"

Hetty and Hank listened carefully.

"Come here, young ones, and get your prize."

Hetty held out her hand, and there, shining
up at her, was a bright gold piece.

"Oh, thank you, sir!" cried Hetty and Hank.
"Now we can buy our shining shoes!"

They ran past the beans and corn. They ran through the hustle and bustle of the crowd. They raced along the street until they came to the little red store.

The storekeeper was standing behind the counter.

"We want to buy some beautiful, creaky, squeaky shoes!" said Hank, all out of breath.

The storekeeper got down his brightest shoes, and Hetty and Hank each took a pair that played a creaky, squeaky song.

Then they bought some gifts to take home with them for Granny, Mammy, and Pappy.

Then off they started on the long trip home. Up, up, up they went, round and round the mountain.

After a long, long climb, they reached their own little cabin. There sat Mammy and Pappy and Granny waiting on the porch. How pleased they were to see Hetty and Hank and all the new things they had bought!

The next day was Sunday, so they put on their
beautiful things and went to the meeting house.

Hetty and Hank walked proudly into the meeting house. Their shoes were playing such a creaky, squeaky song that all the people stretched their necks to see who could be wearing such beautiful shoes.